TECHNICAL GRAPHICS

JOHN BEDFORD AND COLIN PYNE

BOOK TWO

John Murray

© John Bedford and Colin Pyne 1985

First published 1985
by John Murray (Publishers) Ltd
50 Albemarle Street, London W1X 4BD

Typeset, printed and bound
in Great Britain at
The Bath Press, Avon

British Library Cataloguing in Publication Data

Bedford, John R.
   Technical graphics.
   Bk. 2
   1. Engineering drawings
   I. Title   II. Pyne, C. A. W.

ISBN 0-7195-4098-4

Contents

Preface

This is the second of two books designed to provide a continuous course over the subject area of Drawing for the Environment, currently described as Graphic Communication. It follows on immediately from the first book, expanding the knowledge gained there up to and including examination work.

To assist in solving its widened field of design and communications problems it further expands the basic geometry section of the first book and introduces a wide coverage of standard type workshop drawings of everyday objects. It explores in some detail the modern 'instant impact' methods of graphic communications by quoting examples of advertising logo and information charting. This is aimed at encouraging original thinking in the design of graphical communication of information over a wide spectrum of modern situations.

ACKNOWLEDGEMENTS

The examination questions at the end of this book are reproduced by kind permission of the Examining Boards listed below, to whom the authors express their grateful acknowledgements.

Associated Examining Board (*AEB*)
University of London (*LU*)
Oxford and Cambridge Schools Examination Board (*O & CSEB*)
Southern Universities Joint Board (*SUJB*)
Welsh Joint Education Committee (*WJEC*)
Associated Lancashire Schools Examination Board (*ALSEB*)
East Anglian Examination Board (*EAEB*)
East Midland Regional Examination Board (*EMREB*)
Southern Region Examination Board (*SREB*)
Welsh Joint Education Committee (*WJEC*)
West Midland Examination Board (*WMEB*)

The authors also express their thanks to M & T Chemicals Ltd for the photograph of electroplating of aluminium on p. 77, and to W. Allday & Co. Ltd, Stourport-on-Severn, Worcestershire, for the illustration of their 'Alcosa' gas and air brazing nozzle on p. 88.

The cover photographs are reproduced by kind permission of Ian Dobbie/The Design Council (lamp) and The Design Council (electronic micrometer).

1 Pictorial Representation

The golden rule when preparing graphic information is to:

LOOK
ANALYSE
DRAW

Looking at the outlines of a number of different manufactured objects shows that when broken down into their simplest component shapes these stem from the three basic shapes of circle, square and triangle.

Figure 1:1 is a flow diagram which shows how the three basic shapes can be developed to create more complicated three-dimensional objects.

A fundamental requirement in all drawing and design is an ability to draw freehand. It will be found extremely helpful if students can gain mastery in the freehand sketching of the basic shapes given below.

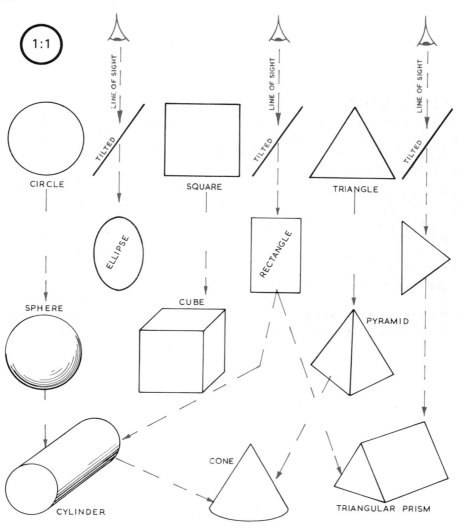

1

FREEHAND DRAWING IN PROPORTION

If the proportions of the finished drawing need to correspond accurately with those of the original then some means of measurement must be used. The easiest one is shown below.

With the arm held straight and at full stretch, hold the pencil as shown in Fig. 1:2, covering the total height of the object between the pencil tip and the thumb. Horizontal distances are measured by rotating the hand only, as in Fig. 1:3.

The pencil can be marked off in fractions between the two overall points to help in establishing smaller proportions such as the width of the windows and the door.

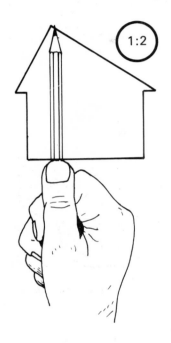

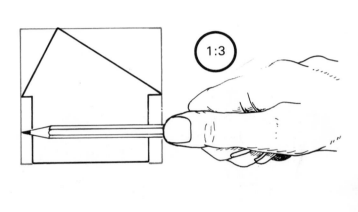

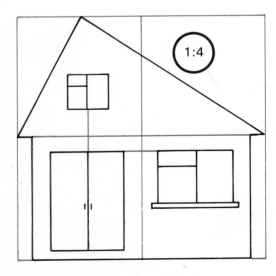

Method for freehand drawing in proportion
Look at Fig. 1:4.
1 Surround the object with an imaginary envelope, in this case a square. Draw this basic shape in proportion as shown above.
2 Divide this surrounding envelope into a grid that coincides with the most important features, in this case four smaller squares.
3 Subdivide these main grid lines to establish the positions of the door and windows.
4 Complete the drawing, line in and erase the grid.

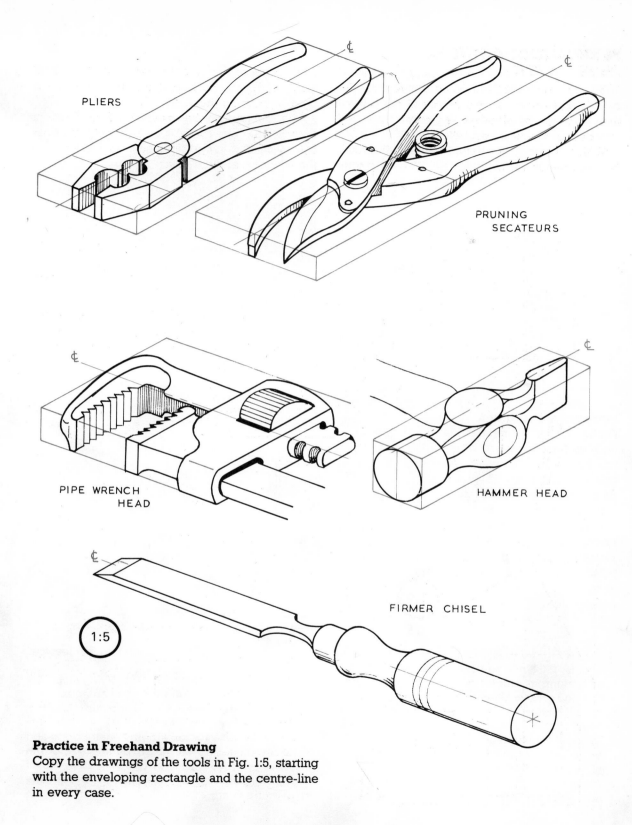

PLIERS

PRUNING
SECATEURS

PIPE WRENCH
HEAD

HAMMER HEAD

FIRMER CHISEL

1:5

Practice in Freehand Drawing
Copy the drawings of the tools in Fig. 1:5, starting
with the enveloping rectangle and the centre-line
in every case.

3

PERSPECTIVE DRAWING

The photograph shows the pilings of a pier going away in the distance to a point where they vanish. Any drawing which gives this type of visual effect may be called **perspective drawing**.

Figure 1:6 shows the top and bottom of the first post of a fence joined to a vanishing point (VP). All posts of the same real height will fit between these two lines on the drawing.

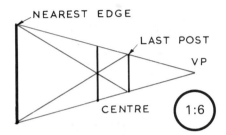

The diagonals drawn as shown between the first and the last fencing posts cross in both the horizontal and the vertical centres of the fence.

Perspective Proportion

Figure 1:7 is a perspective view of a garden fence which has five spaces between the first and last posts. A paved path runs alongside the fence.

It can be clearly seen that the distances between the posts appear less the further away they are. This is true of both vertical and horizontal distances when shown in perspective.

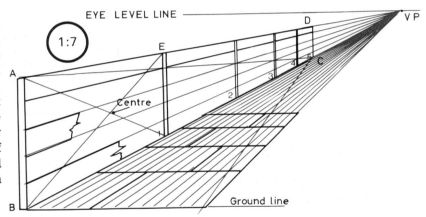

Q1 Draw Fig. 1:7 to a scale of 1:20, when the fence height is 1500 mm and the fence has five equal spaces along its length.

1 Position an eye-level line and a vanishing point on it which is well to the right of the first fence post.
2 Divide the first post (AB) into the same number of divisions as there are gaps in the fence, and project each to the VP.
3 Approximate the end of the fence (CD) and draw one diagonal (AC) which, as it crosses each of the lines, locates a fence post in perspective length.
4 The path has fourteen rows of paving slabs, so divide the ground line into fourteen equal divisions. Draw the diagonal as before and locate the corners of the slabs as shown.

Q2 Draw a tiled floor for a room 4 metres long and 3 metres wide. Choose the shape and size of the tiles yourself. Use a scale of 1:20 with an eye-level line 100 mm above the ground-line which contains the 3-metre width.

SINGLE POINT (ESTIMATED) PERSPECTIVE

As we have seen, similar sized objects appear smaller the further away they are and all objects drawn in perspective behave in the same way. When the eye-level line is placed in a different position, however, the object drawn may appear to be above, level with or below us as shown in Figs 1:8 and 1:9 (heights are estimated).

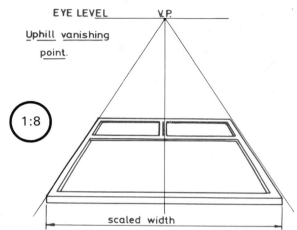

Q3 Draw the window (Fig. 1:8) in single point perspective when the width of the bottom of the window is 2 metres. Choose your own scale and provide your own style of window frame. The height is to be estimated.

Q4 The ceiling of a room has polystyrene tiles 300 mm square. The ceiling is 3 m wide and 3 m long. Draw the ceiling in estimated single point perspective using the downhill vanishing point method shown. Use a scale of 1:20.

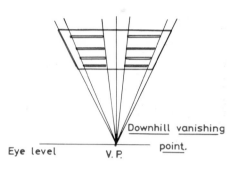

In Figure 1:9 the window is seen from a different position, as the eye-level line shows. In this case the vertical height of the nearest edge is scaled in the same way as the fence in Fig. 1:7. The thickness of the frame is also added in construction lines (green) only.

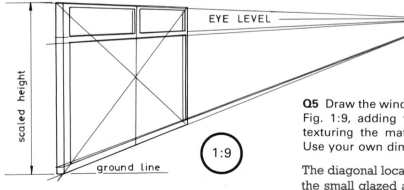

Q5 Draw the window in the new position shown in Fig. 1:9, adding the thickness of the frame and texturing the materials of aluminium and glass. Use your own dimensions.

The diagonal locates the central division between the small glazed areas.

Q6 Draw the door opening into the room where you are working using a suitable scale of your own choice.

Eye Level

The position of the eye-level line relative to the object changes with the changing position of the observer, as shown in Figs. 1:10–1:12.

The three views are all of the same two-door cupboard of the kind that is fastened to the walls of most modern kitchens. In each case it is shown with the doors part-way open. Only the position of the observer, and therefore the eye-level line, has changed.

Note how the nearer edge of the doors appear longer than the edges further away, although we know they are the same length.

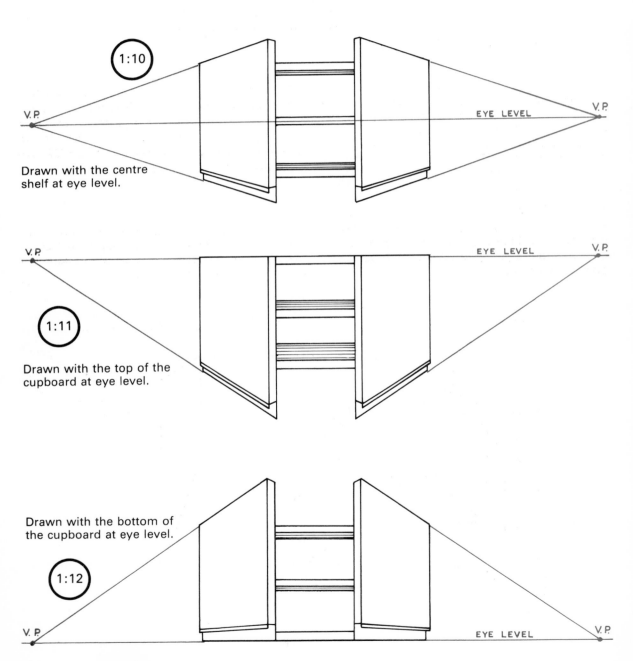

1:10
V.P.
EYE LEVEL
V.P.
Drawn with the centre shelf at eye level.

1:11
V.P.
EYE LEVEL
V.P.
Drawn with the top of the cupboard at eye level.

1:12
Drawn with the bottom of the cupboard at eye level.
V.P.
EYE LEVEL
V.P.

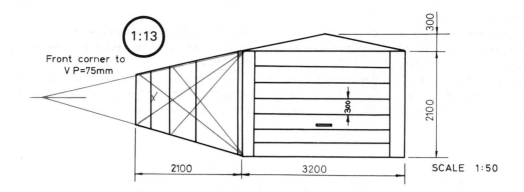

Q7 Draw the garage shown in Fig. 1:13, with the vanishing point 75 mm from the front corner. The garage has four equal divisions of prefabricated concrete along its sides; draw these using perspective proportion. The door is of painted aluminium and you are required to add texture to both the concrete and the door.

Figure 1:14 shows how a room may be drawn in estimated single point perspective as viewed from above. All the lines are either perpendicular or follow the sight lines towards the vanishing point or the centre of vision.

If another item is put into the drawing, but *not* at the same angle as the other features, then it will require two vanishing points in order to obtain the correct perspective view. In Fig. 1:14 the position of the two new vanishing points VP_2 and VP_3 are estimated for the central box.

Q8 Draw a room in perspective, choosing your own eye level (not the same as in Fig. 1:14). Include two windows, a door and an item of furniture that is set at an angle to the walls.

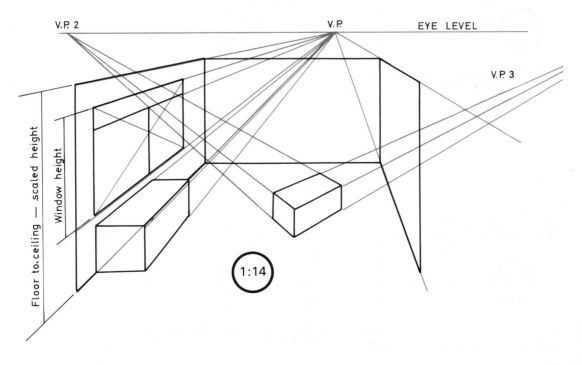

7

ACCURATE SINGLE POINT PERSPECTIVE

In the photograph of tiles on a bathroom wall, the horizontal edges are in perspective and would eventually meet at a vanishing point. This is also true of the vertical edges. Single point perspective deals, as you have seen, with only one vanishing point. In Figs 1:15 and 1:16 the object to be viewed is in a central position and would be on the observer's **centre of vision**.

The VP may be placed anywhere on the eye-level line, as in previous examples.

Q9 Design a tile with a pattern and draw it in accurate single point perspective when the tile is 150 mm × 150 mm × 15 mm thick. The tile should be drawn to a suitable scale and have an uphill vanishing point.

1 Draw the ground line, a centre-line and then (very faint and to scale) the plan of the tile on the ground line (see Fig. 1:15).
2 Locate the observer's position on the centre-line and join corners a and b from the plan above the ground line to the observer's position, locating points 1 and 2 on the ground line.
3 Draw the eye-level line above the plan to the scale being used, locating the VP.

The height of the sight line varies with the position of the observer so this distance will vary considerably.

4 Draw the front view (lightly) over the plan and then join the corners a_1 and b_1 to the VP.
5 Draw verticals from points 1 and 2 to meet the lines from a_1 and b_1 (Fig. 1:16). This locates the perspective lengths of corners a and b to complete the tile.

The horizontal position offers variation in your drawings.

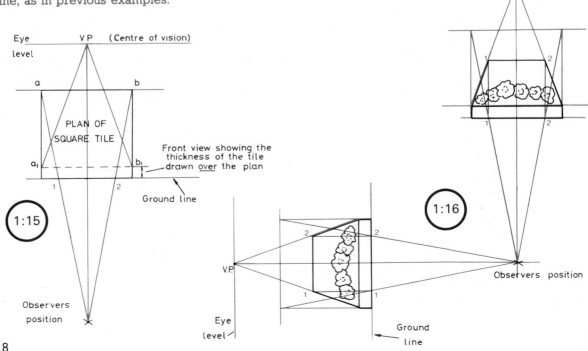

8

Q10 From your own measurements draw a glass-paper block in single point perspective when the observer is looking onto the bevelled edge.

Q11 Draw a set of two steps (Fig. 1:17) to a suitable scale (width 1 m, step height 250 mm). Produce this in single point (accurate) perspective.

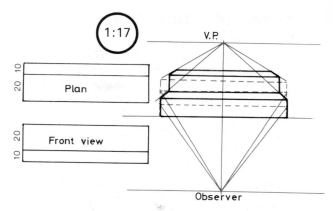

PERSPECTIVE ADVERTISING

Examples in this chapter show that perspective is often used in the visual graphic arts, of which advertising must surely be the most obvious. Study the two drawings below and design either a letter or a pictogram perspective drawing.

Q12 Use your own initials to provide the letters for an advertisement in perspective (see Fig. 1:18).
(a) First draw the letters flat to find the heights of the various parts of each letter.
(b) Estimate where the letters will end and use the perspective division to divide that length into the required number of spaces.

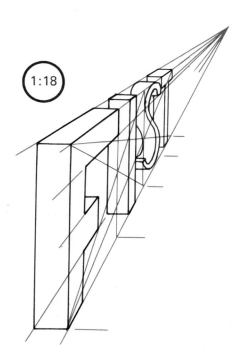

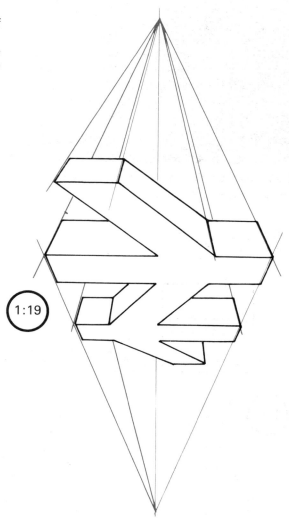

Q13 Design a pictogram that is simple in shape and draw it flat. From this produce a perspective pictogram, giving depth to your drawing as shown in Fig. 1:19.

ARCHITECTURAL PERSPECTIVE

The following drawings show methods of presenting a house (Fig. 1:20) from different angles in estimated perspective.

All heights are scaled from the front corner AB, which is central to VP_1 and VP_2.

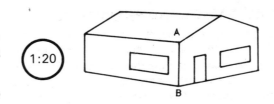

1:20

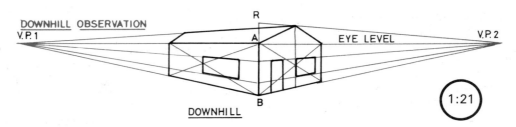

1:21

Study Fig. 1:21 (downhill observation) to understand how the diagonals locate the windows.

AB gives the scaled heights going to vanishing points for door and windows. R gives the height of the ridge.

In Fig. 1:22 (uphill observation) the outlines have been omitted so that construction may be seen.

To find the back corner of the house: Lightly join A to VP_1 and B to VP_2. The top back corner is found where they cross (Fig. 1:23).

To find the ridge at the back: Lightly join B diagonally to the bottom corner. Join C diagonally to the top corner. Draw a vertical through the centre. The back ridge is located where it meets the line from VP_1 to R.

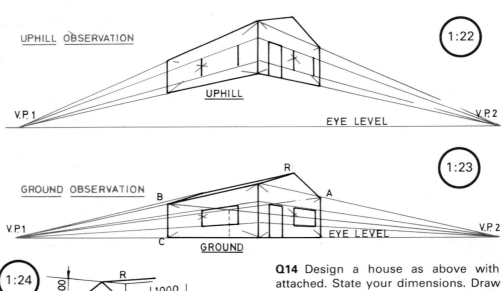

1:22

1:23

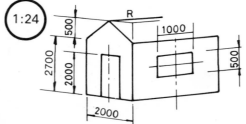

1:24

Q14 Design a house as above with a garage attached. State your dimensions. Draw the house at ground level using estimated perspective with two VPs. Colour your drawing.

Q15 Draw the garden shed (Fig. 1:24) in downhill estimated perspective when the shed is 2 m wide and 4 m long. Use the other dimensions given to estimate proportions.

MEASURED POINT PERSPECTIVE

Measured point perspective is the most accurate method of perspective drawing since all distances are scaled. It uses the angles of 30° and 60° to locate the vanishing points with the centre of vision originating from the observer's position.

Q16 Draw a cooker housing (Figs 1:25 and 1:26) that is 2 m high, 600 mm wide and 600 mm deep using measured point perspective and scale 1:20.

1 Draw the eye-level line and at scaled distances below it draw the ground line and a light line for the observer's position. Eye level = 1.6 m; observer to front corner (on ground line) = 2.5 m.
2 From the left-hand side draw a line at 30° to the eye-level line to locate the observer's position.
3 From the observer's position draw at 60° line to the eye-level line to locate VP2, and a vertical line for the centre of vision. Draw in the front corner AB to a scale of 1:20.

4 **To locate measuring points MP1 and MP2 (Fig. 1:27)**: Draw an arc with centre VP1 and radius to the observer's position to locate point MP1 on the eye-level line. Locate MP2 by using VP2 in the same way.
5 On the ground line mark scaled divisions (scale 1:20) on both sides of the front corner AB to give 100 mm distances.
6 From A and B (i.e. top and bottom of the front corner) draw light lines to the vanishing points in the normal way.
7 To obtain the correct width of 600 mm, draw a line from the 600 mm (scaled) mark on the left-hand side of the ground line to MP1. To obtain the depth of 600 mm draw a line from the ground line as shown to MP2.
8 Where the line to VP1 crosses the line to MP1 the corner width is found. The lines to MP2 and VP2 locate the depth.
9 From these corners draw verticals to complete the drawing.

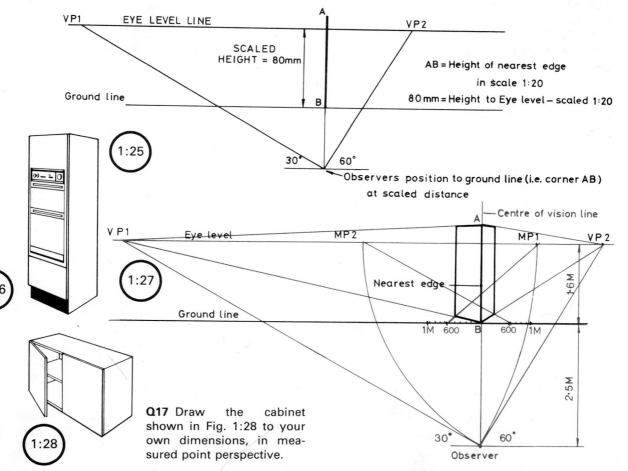

EYE LEVEL LINE

SCALED HEIGHT = 80mm

Ground line

AB = Height of nearest edge in scale 1:20

80 mm = Height to Eye level – scaled 1:20

30° 60°

Observers position to ground line (i.e. corner AB) at scaled distance

1:25

Centre of vision line

VP1 Eye level MP2 MP1 VP2

1:27

Nearest edge

Ground line

1M 600 B 600 1M

1.6M

2.5M

30° 60°

Observer

26

1:28

Q17 Draw the cabinet shown in Fig. 1:28 to your own dimensions, in measured point perspective.

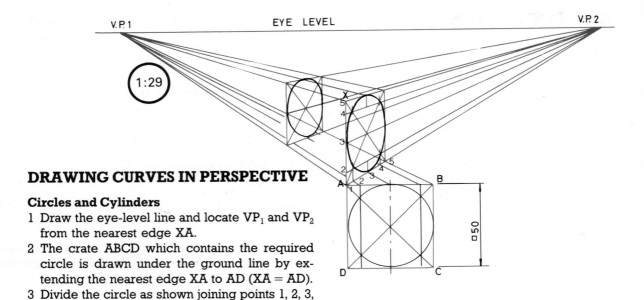

1:29

DRAWING CURVES IN PERSPECTIVE

Circles and Cylinders

1 Draw the eye-level line and locate VP_1 and VP_2 from the nearest edge XA.

2 The crate ABCD which contains the required circle is drawn under the ground line by extending the nearest edge XA to AD (XA = AD).

3 Divide the circle as shown joining points 1, 2, 3, 4 and 5 to VP_1, from AB.

4 Transfer the divisions 1, 2, 3, 4 and 5 to XA and join these points to VP_2. The intersection points will locate the perspective circle.

Q18 Draw the circles in Fig. 1:29 and join both circles together to form a cylinder.

Q19 Draw a protractor radius 50 mm in perspective to a scale of 1:2 and show the angles of 30°, 60°, 120° and 150°.

Arcs

Q20 Draw the Woodruff key (Fig. 1:30) to the given sizes. Use the method of Fig. 1:29.

Always draw the circle or arc *first* and then enclose it in the crate for locating points. The diagonal lines will locate points where they cross the circle or arc.

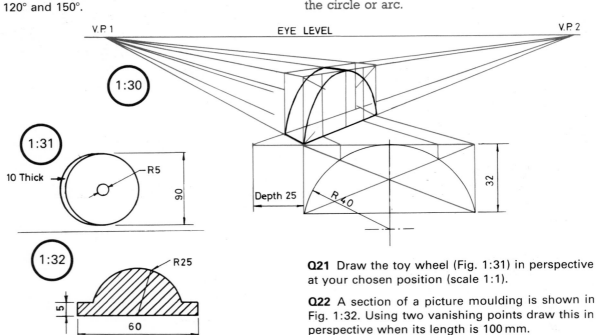

1:30

1:31

10 Thick — R5

90

1:32

R25

5

60

Depth 25   R40

32

Q21 Draw the toy wheel (Fig. 1:31) in perspective at your chosen position (scale 1:1).

Q22 A section of a picture moulding is shown in Fig. 1:32. Using two vanishing points draw this in perspective when its length is 100 mm.

PERSPECTIVE GRIDS

Sketching Grids

A perspective sketching grid makes perspective drawings quicker and easier to complete as well as enabling the designer to choose the angles and maintain them throughout the drawing.

Figures 1:33 and 1:34 are drawn on grids where two vanishing points are used and the scale is drawn on the central vertical line. These are both examples of estimated perspective as the backward distances are *not* in perspective scale, but at least they enable a reasonable perspective draw-ing to be achieved. Students may use this method to become familiar with perspective drawing although bearing in mind that it is not an accurate method.

Accurate Single Point Perspective Grids

The front face of objects drawn using these grids should lie on the scaled picture plane as shown in Fig. 1:35. This should therefore be drawn first. The height and receding lines are then in perspective scale (Fig. 1:36) and may be drawn in by using the self-explanatory graphic method. This grid may be used for downwards (plan views) and front (diminishing) views of objects.

The grid may be increased by extending the perspective lines and enclosing them in rectang-les (Fig. 1:36).

Q23 Draw a plan of a bathroom 3.2 m × 2 m × 2.5 m high using a scaled picture plane where 10 mm represents 200 mm. Include the following: bath, WC, wash basin, window, door. (For the plan of a bathroom this size the picture plane should be the largest rectangle.)

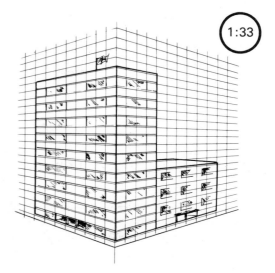

1:33

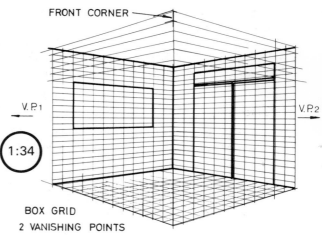

FRONT CORNER

V.P.1   V.P.2

1:34

BOX GRID
2 VANISHING POINTS

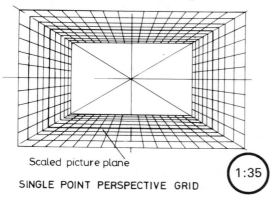

Scaled picture plane

1:35

SINGLE POINT PERSPECTIVE GRID

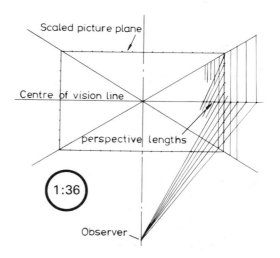

Scaled picture plane

Centre of vision line

perspective lengths

1:36

Observer

13

Two Point Perspective Grids

This type of grid produces accurate perspective scale lengths within a grid system. To draw this grid follow the method given below (see Fig. 1:37).

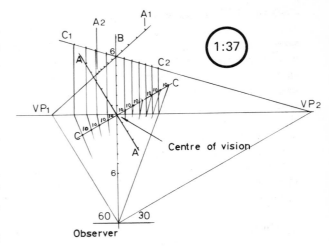

1 Draw a horizontal line (the eye-level line) and a vertical line (axis B) meeting at the centre of vision.
2 Draw the two axes AA and CC through the centre of vision, one at 60° and the other at 30° to the eye-level line. These form the plan of the perspective drawing.
3 Scale the three axes A, B and C, working from the centre of vision. Use a scale of 10 mm = 3 m for a drawing of a 12-storey building, i.e. each of the 12 divisions on B represents 3 m.
4 Locate the observer's position as shown and draw lines parallel to the axes AA and CC to locate VP_1 and VP_2.

To find perspective distances CC

1 Draw a light line from VP_2 through the top scaled height 6 on B and extend this line.
2 From the scale points on CC draw light lines to the observer's position, marking where they cross the eye-level line.
3 Draw verticals through these points on the eye-level line to locate perspective lengths between C_1 and C_2.

To find perspective distances AA

1 Draw a line from the top scaled height 6 on B to VP_1.
2 From the scale points on AA draw lines to the observer's position to cross the eye-level line.
3 Draw verticals through these points to locate perspective distances between A_1 and A_2.

These constructions may also be drawn from bottom positions (uphill observation). Only one of the four possible angles has been used. Note that there are scaled distances on all four arms from the centre of the axes (Fig. 1:38).

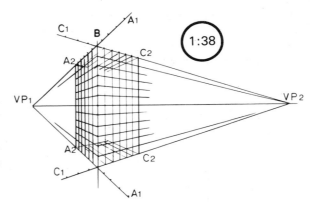

Q24 Draw a perspective grid where 10 mm = 1 m to a total of 6 m in any direction and a total height of 10 m when eye level is centred at height 5 m as in Fig. 1:38. Draw over this grid (or part of it) two patio doors that are 2 m high and have a total width of 3 m.

Q25 Draw a perspective grid suitable for drawing a TV set that is 650 mm wide, 450 mm high and 450 mm deep. (On the construction drawing B = 450 mm; A and C are the other measurements, depending on the angle you choose.)
Draw the TV set and control panel.

Figure 1:39 shows a completed two point grid containing an accurate perspective drawing of a wall cupboard. Note that each division on the scaled perspective lines represents 50 mm. The grid and drawing is produced over the plan of the axes and the initial construction lines by using set squares and marking points rather than actually drawing lines to:

1 the observer
2 the axes AA and CC
3 the final perspective lines GC_2 and A_1A_2.

With the grid drawn, the object is lined in by following the grid.

Q26 Draw the cupboard on a full A3 sheet where 10 mm represents 50 mm and the cupboard is 550 mm high, 350 mm wide and 350 mm deep.

Figure 1:40 shows an accurate perspective drawing of a proposed kitchen layout. This grid is identical to those already shown. The grid lines at the front of the perspective grid have been removed and are shown only at the sides where needed. This type of grid is used by kitchen designers and architects.

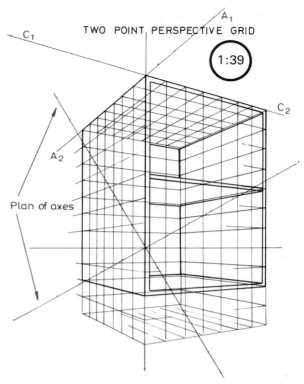

TWO POINT PERSPECTIVE GRID

1:39

Plan of axes

Q27 Using a suitable scale, design and draw an accurate perspective drawing of a small kitchen showing two walls and a selection of fittings.

1:40

ISOMETRIC PROJECTION

The two point perspective method (pages 10–12) produces realistic drawings, but in many cases

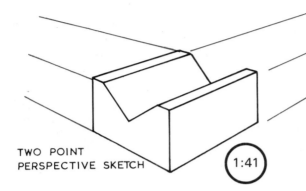

TWO POINT
PERSPECTIVE SKETCH   1:41

1:42   ISOMETRIC
PROJECTION

these can be both difficult and time-consuming to execute. For these reasons draughtsmen often use drawing instruments to help them to produce pictorial drawings. The commonest method used is **isometric projection**, shown in Fig. 1:42 and contrasted with the two point perspective view of the same object in Fig. 1:41.

To make an isometric drawing of the vee block

1 Draw the three basic lines (Fig. 1:43), making them equal to the height, length and width of the object ($30 \times 40 \times 40$).
2 Join the three lines to produce a box equal to the overall size of the object (Fig. 1:44).

This isometric box is made up of six lines at 30° to the horizontal and three vertical lines, making three sets of parallel lines, all of true length.

3 Insert the two lines which mark the edge of the vee cut (Fig. 1:45).
4 Copy the front view shown in Fig. 1:46. Use a 45° set square to draw the vee groove.
5 Using dividers, transfer the distance AB to the centre-line on the front face of the box.
6 Join B to the top edges of the vee groove.
7 Draw the oblique line on the rear face parallel to its companion on the front face.

The use of set squares alone will not reproduce the oblique lines in isometric projections; they always need to be copied by the above method.

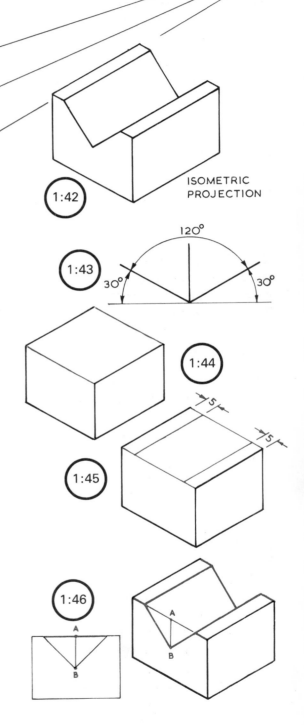

16

When a 45° line on a front face of an isometric drawing links up with an edge on a top face, they will appear as one continuous line. (Note especially Figs 1:47 and 1:48.)

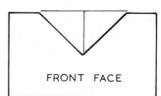

FRONT FACE

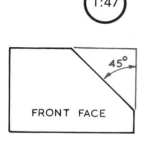

1:47

45°

FRONT FACE

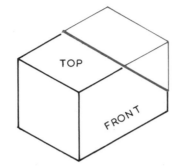

TOP

FRONT

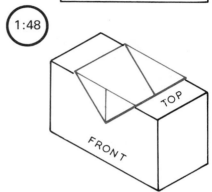

1:48

TOP

FRONT

ISOMETRIC GRIDS

Many objects are easier to draw when use is made of paper on which a pattern of isometric grid lines has been printed, as shown in Fig. 1:49.

Q28 Make a freehand isometric sketch of the cube in the photograph using isometric grid paper.

Figure 1:50 shows the elevation and plan of a cube that has had four of its edges chamfered at 45°.

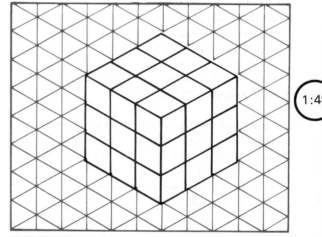

1:49

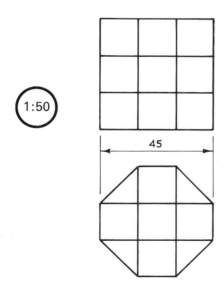

1:50

45

Q29 Make a full size isometric drawing of the octagonal prism.

Drawings containing edge lines angled at 45° do not fit readily onto an isometric grid.

17

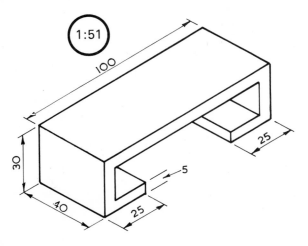

1:51

100

30

40

25

25

5

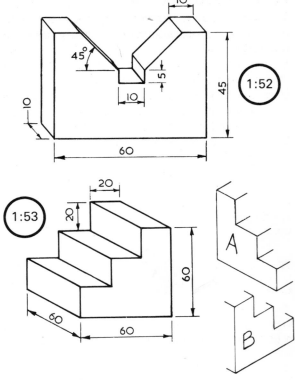

10

45°

5

10

45

10

60

1:52

1:53

20

20

60

60

60

A

B

Q30 Copy the drawing of the suspended ceiling clip in Fig. 1:51.

Q31 Make an isometric drawing of the drilling machine vee block in Fig. 1:52.

Q32 Make two isometric drawings of the model steps shown in Fig. 1:53, the first with front face A, the second with front face B.

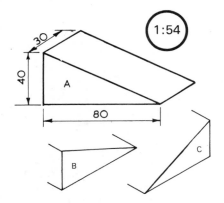

1:54

30

40

A

80

B

C

Q33 Make two isometric drawings of the wedge in Fig. 1:54, the first with face A as shown in sketch B, and the second as shown in sketch C.

Q34 Make an isometric drawing of the machine vice body shown in Fig. 1:55.

Q35 Make an isometric drawing of a 100 mm length of the sash bar in Fig. 1:56.

All these exercises can be drawn on isometric grid paper, but will look much clearer on plain drawing paper.

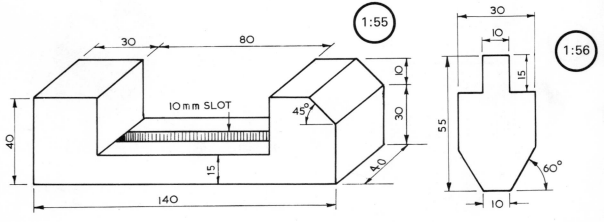

1:55

30

80

10mm SLOT

45°

10

30

40

40

15

140

30

10

15

1:56

55

60°

10

PROPORTIONS

To represent an object correctly it is essential to draw its proportions accurately. The balance of the length, width and height in the drawing must be exactly the same as the object. An easy method of ensuring that these are correct is to start by drawing a box to the same size as the overall size of the object and then fitting the drawing into this box. It also helps to divide up the box with grid lines which correspond to the main features of the object. In very many cases a centre-line is essential.

Q36 Copy the drawing of the saw horse (Fig. 1:57), starting with the outer rectangle and the centre-line.

Q37 Copy the drawing of the lab stool (Fig. 1:58). Insert a suitable hole in the centre of the top to facilitate picking up and carrying the stool.

Q38 Copy the drawing of the stand steps (Fig. 1:59). Design and show a suitable attachment which will keep the legs open at the angle shown.

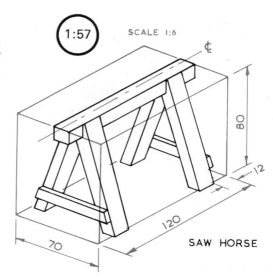

SCALE 1:6

SAW HORSE

FIVE MAJOR PIECES 12 x 8

TWO END BRACES 8 x 4 —10mm ABOVE BASE LEVEL

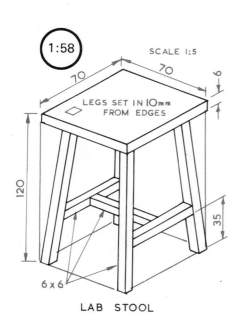

SCALE 1:5

LEGS SET IN 10mm FROM EDGES

LAB STOOL

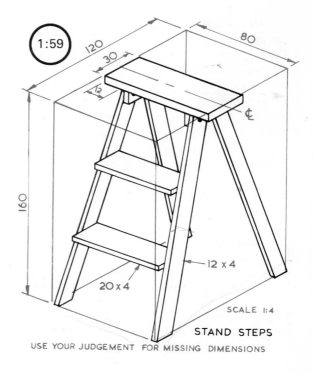

SCALE 1:4

STAND STEPS

USE YOUR JUDGEMENT FOR MISSING DIMENSIONS

19

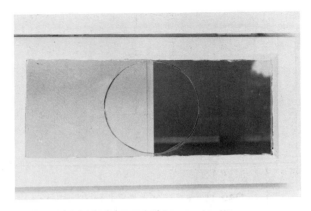

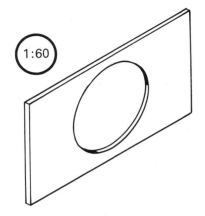

THE CIRCLE AND ISOMETRIC PROJECTION

The photograph shows a kitchen window-pane with a circular hole ready to take an extractor fan. Figure 1:60 shows an isometric view of the same window-pane. From this it can be seen that when a circle is drawn in isometric projection it becomes distorted to form an ellipse.

To project an ellipse from a circle by means of ordinates (Fig. 1:61):

Ordinates are lines which transfer dimensions from one view to another.

1 Draw the circle and its centre-lines AB and CD.
2 Divide AB into four equal parts AE, EO, OF, FB.
3 Draw the centre-line ab of the ellipse at 30°.
4 Project points A and B to cut this centre-line, thus establishing the length of the major axis.
5 Project ordinates across the circle through E and F to cut the major axis in e and f.
6 Using dividers, step off the distances E1, E2, F1 and F2 along the respective ordinates as e1, e2, f1 and f2, thus obtaining four points on the curve of the ellipse.
7 Similarly step off the distances OC and OD on the circle to give oc and od on the ellipse.

If the ellipse is small a smooth curve can be drawn through these eight points to complete the figure. If the ellipse is so large that it is difficult to draw an accurate curve around the ends of the major axis then additional ordinates can be drawn through G (the mid-point of AE) and H (the mid-point of FH) and the length of these lines transferred to the ellipse in the same way.

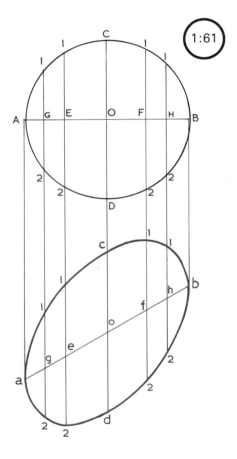

When a circle is projected to form an ellipse the vertical dimensions remain the same.

20

Q39 Make an isometric drawing of the towel hook in Fig. 1:62. Show the 45° lip at the bottom right-hand corner of the drawing.

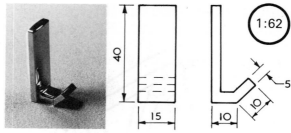

1:62

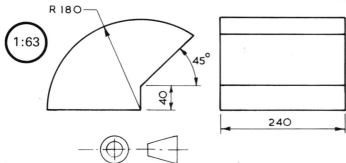

1:63

Q40 Make a one-third size isometric drawing of the central heating roof vent in Fig. 1:63.

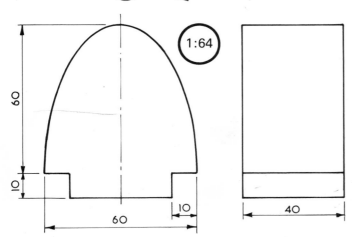

1:64

Q41 Make a full size isometric drawing of the rubber car-axle buffer (Fig. 1:64). The curve is a half-ellipse.

Q42 The two views in Fig. 1:65 show part of a motor cycle crankshaft forging. Make a full size isometric drawing of the outline of one of the flanges. Omit the shaft and holes.

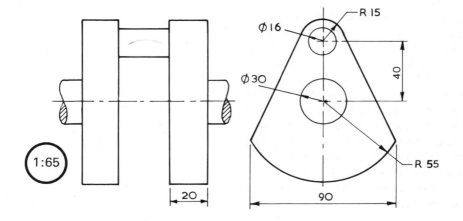

1:65

OBLIQUE PROJECTIONS

Projecting circles to assist in the development of ellipses is very time-consuming. To save time **oblique projection** is used to make a drawing of an object containing circles and arcs (e.g. Fig. 1:66). This method enables all these curves to be drawn with compasses.

Figure 1:67A is an isometric projection of a cube and Fig. 1:67B is a **cavalier** oblique projection of the same cube. If you carefully measure all eighteen lines you will find that they are all the same length. Yet our eyes suggest that the sloping lines in B are longer than those in A. To overcome this illusion it is customary to halve the length of the sloping lines, as in Fig. 1:67C, to make the drawing appear the right size. This adjusted drawing is called a **cabinet** oblique projection.

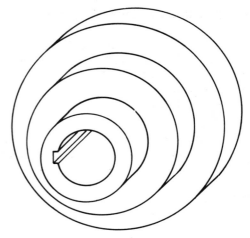

THREE SPEED LATHE PULLEY

1:66

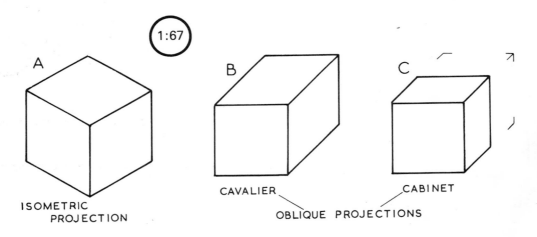

1:67

A

ISOMETRIC
PROJECTION

B

CAVALIER

C

CABINET

OBLIQUE PROJECTIONS

A further comparison of the three drawings will show that the front faces of both oblique projections appear smaller than similar faces on the isometric projection. This is also because our eyes read the oblique lines as being longer than the other lines. When it is necessary for an isometric view to appear the right size the dimensions are reduced by using an **isometric scale** (Fig. 1:68). In this scale the 45° line is marked off with the main dimensions needed for the drawing. Verticals are then dropped to a 30° line to give the equivalent isometric distances (a reduction of 1:0.816).

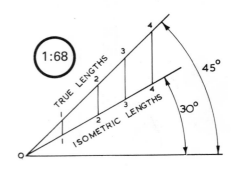

1:68

TRUE LENGTHS
ISOMETRIC LENGTHS
45°
30°
O

Drawing a bearing bush in cabinet oblique projection

1 Draw the centre-lines and add the two front face circles ($R = 15$ and $R = 20$) as in Fig. 1:69.
2 Draw the 45° axis (Fig. 1:70). Mark in the rear centre-lines at the appropriate distance.
3 Draw an arc to show the rear edge of the bush (Fig. 1:71).
4 Draw lines at 45° tangential to both the circle and the arc. Line in the drawing to complete it (Fig. 1:72).

Always draw circles and arcs first, and then add the straight connecting lines.

Q43 Make a full size cabinet oblique projection of the scaled-down racing car wheel chock (Fig. 1:73).

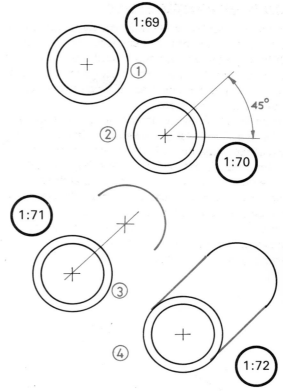

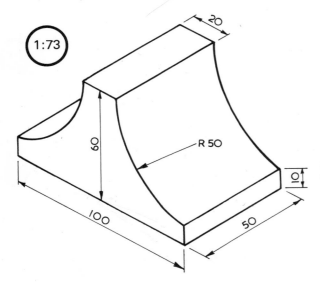

Q44 Make a full size cabinet oblique drawing of the Woodruff key (Fig. 1:74).

Q45 Make a full size cabinet oblique drawing of the pipe clip in Fig. 1:75.

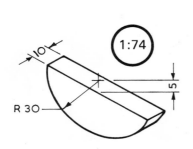

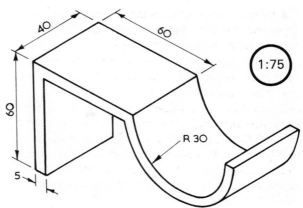

PLANOMETRIC PROJECTION

In this method of drawing, also called **architectural axonometric projection**, the two axes which represent horizontal lines are set at any two complementary angles, e.g. 45° and 45° or 30° and 60°. Views drawn by this method have the advantage of starting from a true plan from which verticals are drawn to produce a pictorial view.

Figure 1:76 is a planometric projection of a fitted kitchen and gives the impression of being viewed from a high point.

This method is particularly suitable for showing details of both the interior and the exterior of a building in one view.

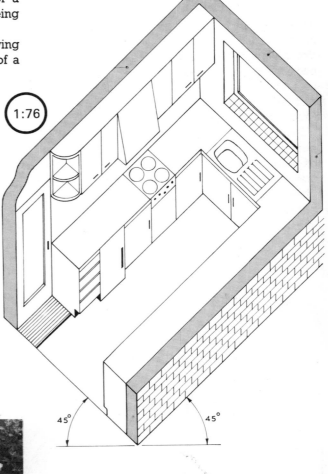

Q46 Make a one-quarter size planometric projection of the garden barbecue shown in the photograph. The large slabs measure 600 × 600 × 38 mm; the bricks measure 230 × 75 × 38 mm.

EXPLODED VIEWS

1:77

1:78

1:79

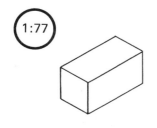

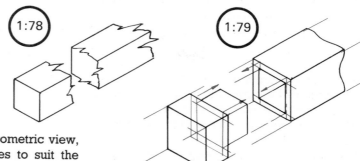

These may be drawn to show an isometric view, an oblique view, or at other angles to suit the draughtsman. Construction lines are needed in all cases to draw the object in its exploded position (see Fig. 1:79) so that new corners, centre-lines and edges are seen to be in line with their previous positions.

Figure 1:80 shows an isometric drawing of a pencil sharpener with its parts lifted out or in exploded positions. The main body is drawn first, then the projection lines of the parts are located. These parts are then 'lifted' out of their normal positions by using centre-lines and projection lines.

1:80

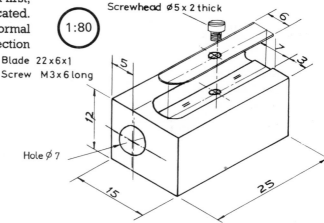

Screwhead ⌀5 x 2 thick
Blade 22x6x1
Screw M3x6 long
Hole ⌀ 7
6
7
3
5
12
15
25

60
45
20
10
⌀40
5
20
5
10
10

1:81

Q47 Draw an isometric view of the pencil sharpener in Fig. 1:80 to the scale of 3:1 with its parts exploded as shown. Add five main dimensions to your drawing.

Q48 Figure 1:81 shows the end fittings of a neon light in third-angle projection and also in exploded pictorial form.

Produce a full size isometric drawing of both ends of the strip light using the centre-line method to locate positions as shown.

The light tube has a metal cap, diameter 32 mm and 10 mm long, and a glass of diameter 38 mm. The thickness of the end retainers need not be shown. Estimate the sizes of the pins and plate not dimensioned. Add six main dimensions to your drawing.

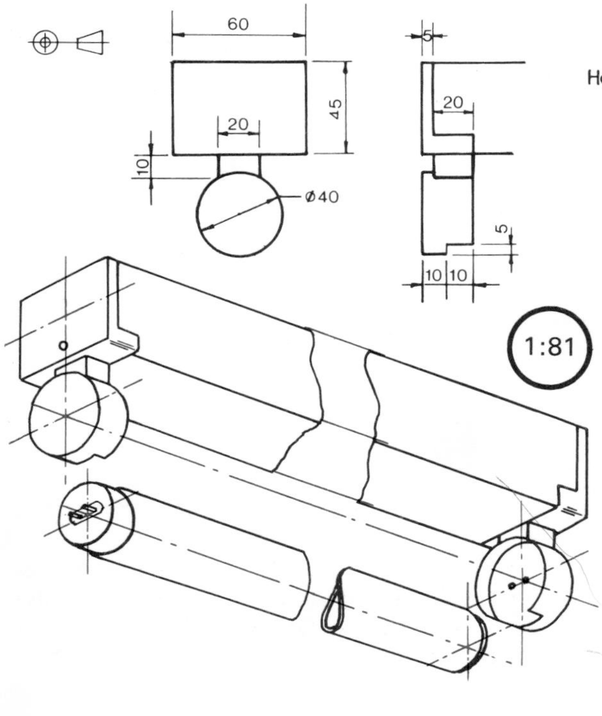

2 Building Drawings

A building drawing is produced to give information to a variety of professional people involved in agreeing, checking and building a particular structure. Because of the vast amount of information included on these drawings, symbols are used to save space and to keep the drawing as clear as possible.

The symbols in the table opposite have been taken from *Recommendations for Building Drawing Practice, BS 1192* and cover the basic requirements. Should further information or symbols be required the complete list, which is very extensive, may be obtained from the British Standards Institute, 2 Park Street, London W1Y 4AA.

Lines

A guide to the recommended thickness of lines may also be found in BS 1192, which suggests that three different thicknesses should be used. In actual line thickness these are described as: 0.2 mm, 0.4 mm, and 0.8 mm.

It is difficult, of course, to obtain thicknesses of 0.2 mm and 0.8 mm with a single pencil, but the aim is obvious, i.e. to have a clearly contrasting series of lines on a drawing to aid clarity. The following style is recommended:

Thin lines—no more than 0.2 mm in thickness.
Medium lines—twice the thickness of thin lines.
Thick lines—twice the thickness of medium lines.

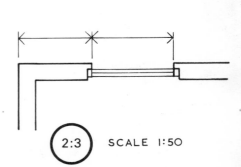

2:1   SCALE 1:1250

2:2   SCALE 1:200

2:3   SCALE 1:50

Block Plan
A block plan locates the site position (Fig. 2:1).
    Thick lines: site outline for new building.
    Medium lines: existing building.
    Thin lines: leader lines, hatching, dimension lines, etc.

Site Plan
A site plan outlines the site or new building (Fig. 2:2).
    Thick lines: outlines of site or new buildings.
    Medium lines: boundaries and general details.
    Thin lines: grid and leader lines, dimension lines, etc.

Location Plan
A location plan shows the positions of spaces within the building (Fig. 2:3).
    Thick lines: loadbearing walls (normally all exterior walls).
    Medium lines: internal partitions, windows, doors, etc.
    Thin lines: grid and leader lines, dimension lines, etc.

BUILDING DRAWING SYMBOLS

(Extracted from BS 1192 by permission of the British Standards Institute, 2 Park Street, London W1Y 4AA.)

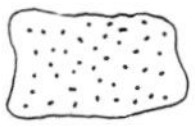

Symbol	Description
	Grassed area
	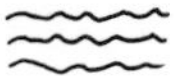 Paved area
	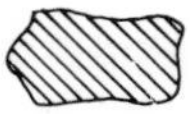 Planted area
	 New trees planted
	 Existing trees
	 Existing tree to be removed
	 Wood
	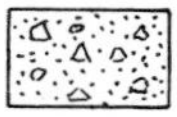 Concrete
	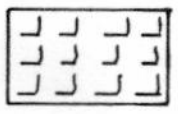 Tiles
	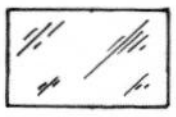 Glass
	 Points to North
M H	Manhole (soil), e.g. bath, sink, WC
M H	Manhole (surface), e.g. rainwater from road, pavement and roof
R WP	Rainwater pipe (down gutterpipes)
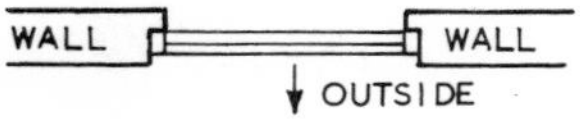 WALL — WALL ↓ OUTSIDE	Window
	 Sliding doors

Symbol	Description
S	Sink
	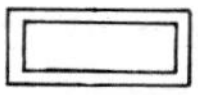 Bath
 WB	Wash basin
S	Shower
	WC
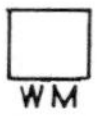 WM	Washing machine
	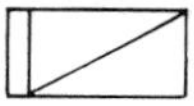 Bed
	 Table
	Chair
	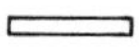 Radiator
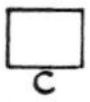 C	Cooker
R	Refrigerator
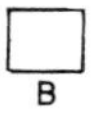 B	Boiler

Electrical

Symbol	Description
	Power point
	Switched socket (outlet)
	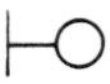 Wall lamp
	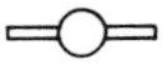 Neon (strip) light
	 Switch
	Pull switch
△	Telephone

27

BLOCK PLAN

Figure 2:4 is a **block plan**: it identifies the site and locates the outline of the building in relation to the surrounding area, e.g. a town plan. The shaded area in the figure can be easily located using the additional surrounding information which is all presented at a suitable scale.

Q1 Copy the block plan (Fig. 2:4) to a suitable scale, adding the scale chosen. Pay particular attention to line thicknesses.

The block plan is often included on the site plan or the location plan, both to aid the District Building Inspectors to find the building and to ensure that building regulations regarding the adjacent buildings and other factors governing the environment are upheld.

Scales suitable for block plans:
1:2500 or 1 mm: 2.5 m
1:1250 or 1 mm: 1.25 m

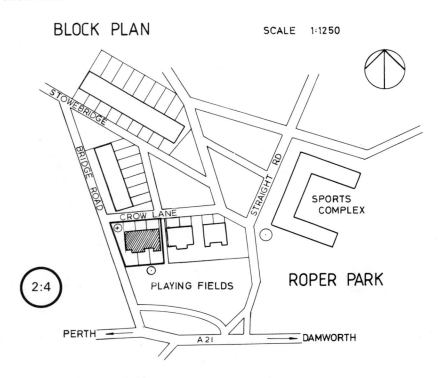

BLOCK PLAN   SCALE   1:1250

2:4

Symbols and Abbreviations

 Points North

 Housing block in question

 Road

 Existing trees

 New trees (planted)

SITE PLAN

A **site plan** locates the position of buildings and includes access roads, drainage, services and general layouts of the site in relation to its immediate surroundings.

Q2 Draw the site plan (Fig. 2:5) enclosed by Crow Lane and Bridge Road, the drainage services and major dimensions. Use a scale of 1:200.

Line thicknesses should be taken from BS 1192.

Scales suitable for site plans:
1:500 or 2 mm: 1 m
1:200 or 5 mm: 1 m

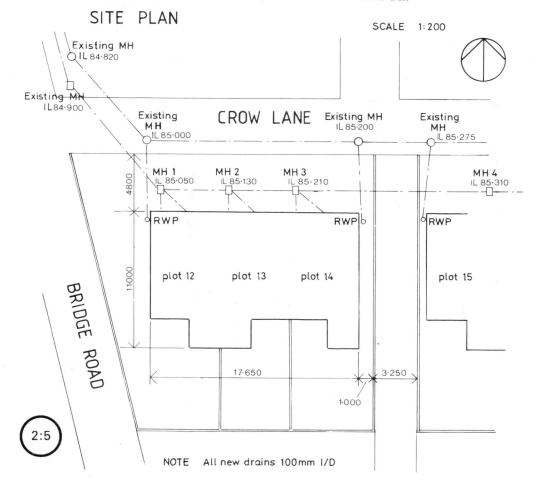

SITE PLAN   SCALE 1:200

Existing MH
IL 84·820

Existing MH
IL 84·900

Existing MH
IL 85·000

CROW LANE

Existing MH
IL 85·200

Existing MH
IL 85·275

MH 1   IL 85·050
MH 2   IL 85·130
MH 3   IL 85·210
MH 4   IL 85·310

4·800

11·000

RWP   RWP   RWP

plot 12   plot 13   plot 14   plot 15

BRIDGE ROAD

17·650   3·250

1·000

2:5

NOTE   All new drains 100mm I/D

Symbols and Abbreviations

MH
☐ Manhole (soil)

RWP
◯ Rainwater pipe

I/D   Inside diameter

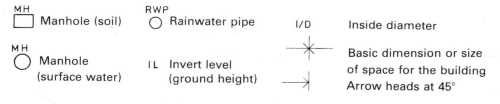

MH
◯ Manhole (surface water)

IL   Invert level (ground height)

Basic dimension or size of space for the building
Arrow heads at 45°

LOCATION PLAN

The **location plan** shows the positions of the various rooms and spaces in the building. It also shows the general construction details of the assembled building.

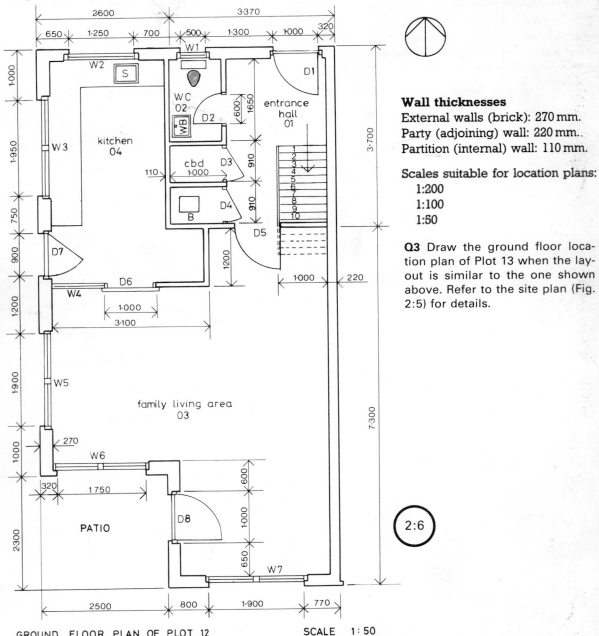

GROUND FLOOR PLAN OF PLOT 12   SCALE   1 : 50

Wall thicknesses
External walls (brick): 270 mm.
Party (adjoining) wall: 220 mm.
Partition (internal) wall: 110 mm.

Scales suitable for location plans:
   1:200
   1:100
   1:50

Q3 Draw the ground floor location plan of Plot 13 when the layout is similar to the one shown above. Refer to the site plan (Fig. 2:5) for details.

Q4 Draw the plan of the kitchen shown above to a scale of 1:50 and include the following fittings: washing machine, refrigerator, larder, sink, cooker; also include a suitable number of wall and floor cupboards.

Q5 Draw the family living area in the location plan above to a scale of 1:50, showing the access doors, windows and also items of furniture that would suitably furnish the room. All items must be drawn to scale.

MODULAR GRIDS

Figure 2:7 shows a bungalow drawn to a scale of 1:100 on 10 mm squares. This drawing is made on a modular planning grid.

Carefully study the drawing, paying particular attention to access to the rooms. If there are any changes you would make, note them down before answering the questions below.

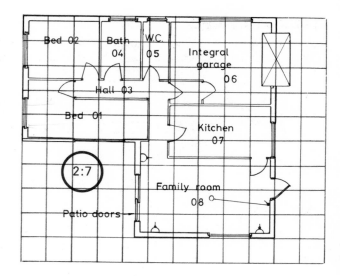

Q6 Produce the drawing of the bungalow (Fig. 2:7) using a 10 mm grid and a scale of 1:50, i.e. 10 mm represents 500 mm. Include in your drawing any changes you have decided upon and also add the basic fittings such as sink, bath, cooker, bed, etc.

Q7 Draw the rooms and enclosures in Fig. 2:7 with the reference numbers and the internal measurements in metres. Add light switches and power points to all rooms in suitable positions (they are already inserted in Family Room 08). BS 1192 symbols should be used.

Q8 Enlarge the patio to twice the size shown in Fig. 2:7 and design a layout that includes shaped and coloured slabs and two raised brick-built flower troughs.

Q9 Figure 2:8 is a modular grid with a line drawing of a bungalow. Use the grid as a basis for measurements and produce a 1:50 scaled drawing including the following:
(a) External and internal wall thicknesses (see page 30).
(b) Windows suitably placed and of a suitable size.
(c) Built-in wardrobes.
(d) Internal doors (indicating the swing of the doors).
(e) Sliding or patio-type doors.

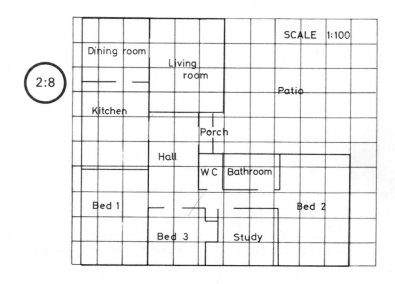

31

A BEDSIT FLAT

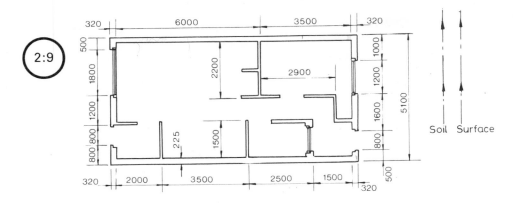

Q10 The basic sizes of a bedsit flat have been given in Fig. 2:9. Draw the flat to a scale of 1:50 and fit in and name the following areas:
(a) Living room.
(b) Kitchen.
(c) Bathroom.
(d) Bed space.
(e) Doors and cupboards in suitable places.
Use BS 1192 symbols. Measurements not given are left to your discretion.

Abbreviations

B = bath
WB = wash basin
WC = toilet
VP = vent pipe
S = sink
RWP = rainwater (surface) pipe
(MH) = surface water manhole
[MH] = soil water manhole
—·— = pipe to carry water
TG = trapped gulley (earthenware/plastic with an 'S' bend to collect sink solid waste and prevent drain odours—normally covered by a grid)

A typical layout of waste water removal is shown in Fig. 2:10. Use this type of layout to show how the waste products would be removed from the bedsit (Fig. 2:9).

Q11 Using the abbreviations listed above, add the 'soil water' and 'surface water' pipework to your layout of the bedsit flat.

The **correct symbols** for each of the domestic fittings should also be included.

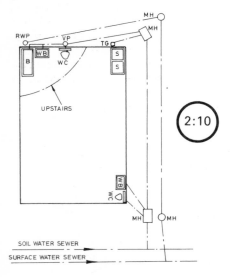

Q12 Figure 2:11 shows a plot of land which is being developed for building different types of houses on different areas of land. The draughtsman has produced a site plan but has left out valuable information.

(a) Draw the site plan to a scale of 1:200 from the information given where the field quadrilateral PRST has a right angle at T.

(b) Find the area of each of the housing plots and then determine the area in square metres of the whole field.

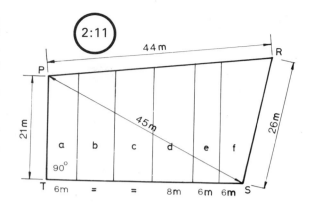

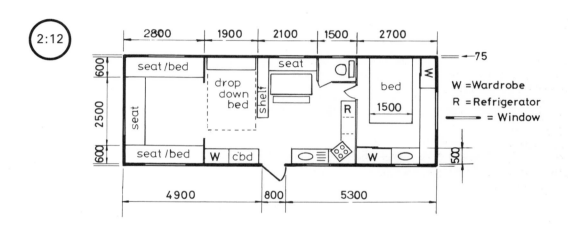

Q13 Figure 2:12 shows the plan of a static caravan to an approximate scale of 1:100.

(a) Draw to a scale of 1:50 a caravan of a similar size that has the layout and equipment necessary to keep a family of two adults and three children in relative comfort. Use the appropriate BS symbols to show fittings. The windows may be indicated as in the diagram. Running water is supplied for the sink and WC. You are to include the drainage pipes.

(b) Draw a suitable circuit that would provide adequate lighting from a 12 V battery supply and draw this as an electric circuit diagram. Only the outline of the caravan is required here.

Q14 The outline of a small caravan is given in Fig. 2:13. Using a scale of 1:50, design the internal layout to sleep two persons and include the following facilities: a sink, a cooker, a fold-down table, a wardrobe, two window seats that may be converted into two single beds, a WC, and a variety of storage areas for food, blankets, cutlery and china.

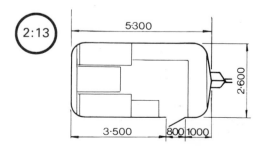

33

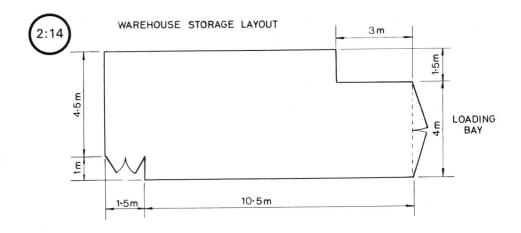

WAREHOUSE STORAGE LAYOUT

Paths and Mazes

Q15 The warehouse shown in Fig. 2:14 is to have racks delivered to hold company stock. Each rack is two metres long and one metre wide and is open on both sides. Study Fig. 2:14, then design a plan of the racks in position showing how staff and delivery men will have easy access to all the racks (a 1 m gap is required for forklift trucks). The path (direction) inside the storage area may be marked with arrows on the floor. State the total number of racks used. Draw the plan to a scale of 1:50.

Q16 Figure 2:15 shows two maze puzzles where one path only may be followed. Design and draw a maze similar to one of these and applying the same principles. Use either an outer circle of diameter 100 mm or a rectangle 100 × 80 mm and allow a 10 mm gap for the path.

Q17 A holiday resort has decided to build a maze in the local gardens. The path is to be 1 m wide, surrounded by a hedge. Design and draw the maze within the area outlined in Fig. 2:16 to a scale of 1:200. Show the hedge as a line. The maze should be parallel with the sides of the plot and the distances AB and BC stated.

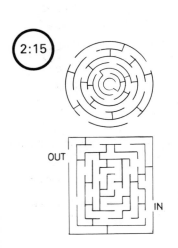

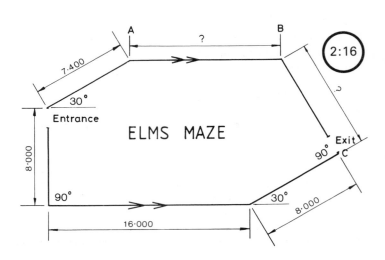

ELMS MAZE

SECTIONS IN BUILDING CONSTRUCTION DRAWING

The following drawings are concerned with actual construction details and show methods of construction. These are not by any means the only methods, but they do at least provide some idea of the ways in which dwellings or shelters may be drawn by the architect in readiness for building.

On drawings of this type colour is often used to identify the different materials shown. There are also texturing techniques recommended by BS 1192 which can be used to distinguish materials.

Figure 2:17 shows the symbols commonly used in building construction drawings with a suggested colour given above each material.

Figure 2:18 is a cutaway drawing to show and name the main parts of the underfloor construction. Note that the **damp-proof course** (DPC) is two courses of brickwork (minimum) above ground level and that the joists are prevented from rot by the underfloor ventilation. This is made possible by airbricks in the back and front house walls and the honeycomb sleeper walls underneath the floor boards and joists which allow the air to circulate. Note the direction of the joists in relation to the sleeper walls.

For private dwellings the **footing bricks** usually extend 1 m below the damp-proof course and sit on concrete footings 200–300 mm deep.

The large **building blocks** are approximately 450 mm × 225 mm × 200 mm. They are high in density with excellent insulation properties and are mainly used in single-storey extensions. The outside of these blocks is covered by a sand and cement mix after building is complete (the blocks are rendered).

The above notes need taking into account when drawing sections through a single-storey house.

Q18 Copy the symbols in Fig. 2:17, enclosing them in rectangles 40 mm × 20 mm and adding the appropriate colour. Take care not to obscure the symbol lines.

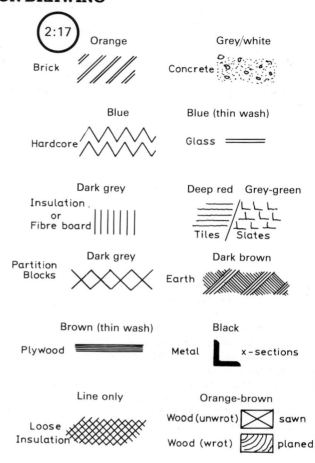

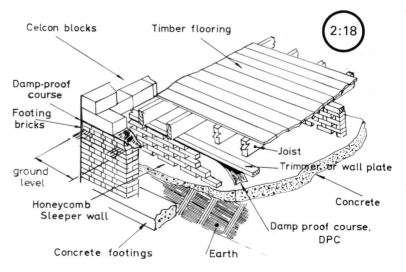

35

Figure 2:19 illustrates a section through a solid floor. The base concrete above the hard-core is covered with a DPM that is linked with the DPC on the outside walls.

DPM stands for damp-proof membrane, a thick polythene sheet or waterproof layer that is spread onto the concrete.

Screed is a thin layer of sand and cement (approximately 50 mm thick) on the DPM to give the smooth floor surface.

The **supporting walls** are of solid brickwork 225 mm thick to a depth of 1 m. The **concrete footings** can vary in size; those shown on the drawing are 500 mm × 250 mm.

Figure 2:20 shows the raised method of floor construction similar to that in Fig. 2:18. The graphic symbols are used to illustrate the materials and maintain a clear and uncluttered drawing. Colour may be added.

Q19 Draw a cross-section across the 5.5 m width of the ware-house in Fig. 2:14. The floor is solid concrete and has a screed 60 mm deep above the DPM. The footings are brickwork, 225 mm thick and 1 m deep, on concrete 600 mm wide and 400 mm deep. Two courses of building blocks should be included above the DPC.

Figure 2:21 shows a part section through the doorway of a wooden garden shed and a pictorial view giving the major dimensions of the whole shed. There are seven underfloor sleepers equally spaced over the 3 m width and four under-floor joists spaced over the 1600 mm depth. The roof is made of 12 mm chipboard, supported by joists running from front to back, and covered by two sheets of damp-proof felt glued in position. The front, back and both sides are frame construc-tions (see the section drawing). The top edge of each side is raised as shown to direct rainwater to the back of the shed.

Q20 Using the major dimension as a guide for internal measurements produce in third-angle projection the following views: (a) a sectional front elevation, (b) a plan view, (c) an end view. Hidden detail is not required and any dimensions not given are left to your own discretion.

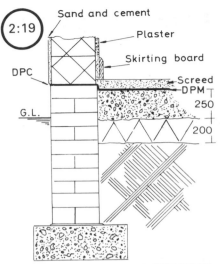

SOLID FLOOR CONSTRUCTION

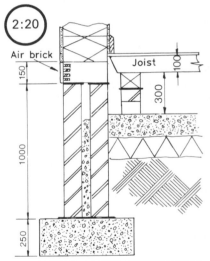

RAISED FLOOR CONSTRUCTION

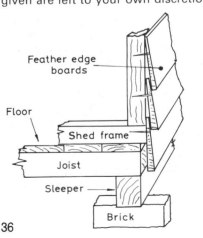

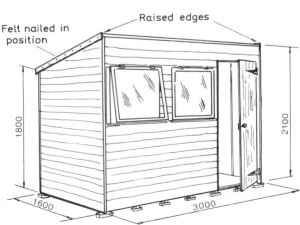

36

3 Graphic Display and Printing

If lettering, symbols, products and information are to be easily understood it is essential that the language used is simple enough for people of all nationalities to read and understand. This concept should be uppermost when the following exercises are undertaken.

Example

An electric iron manufacturer requires an international sign which will show that his product, an electric steam iron, can spray the material before ironing as well as providing the normal steam jets underneath.

The diagram in Fig. 3:1 is a solution to his problem.

Q1 Design a leaflet that shows three different enclosures for door chimes and also indicates the variety of surface textures and sounds available. Figure 3:2 may help you.

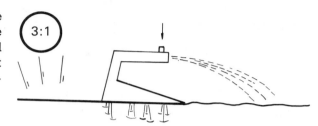

The use of line in all designs should mean that labels are not needed. The line itself is intended to explain the diagram.

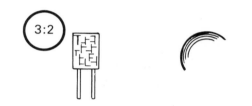

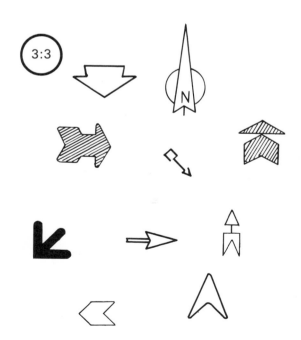

Q2 Anvil Forgecraft Co. require a bold symbol that uses the letter A in a **logogram** or the 'anvil' or 'forgecraft' in a **pictogram**. The Director insists that both the logogram and the pictogram are supplied so that he can choose between them.

Design both the required symbols and then design a third which includes both the letter A and the processes carried out. The shapes should be kept to their most basic outline so that a quick visual impression is formed.

Q3 Use arrows to design an advertisement for a space terminal of the future. It should indicate speed, direction and distance. Some ideas are shown in Fig. 3:3.

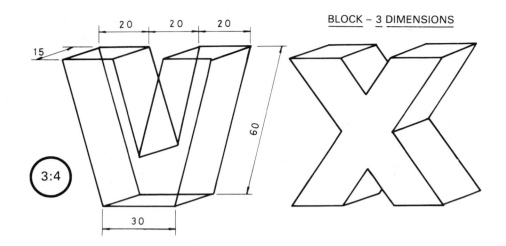

BLOCK – 3 DIMENSIONS

3:4

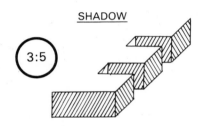

SHADOW

3:5

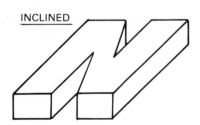

INCLINED

DISPLAY PRINTING

Q4 Use one of the systems in Fig. 3:4 to produce a shop sign to go outside and above a shop window. Use your own name.

Q5 A large company wants its name transferred, in colour, onto its delivery trucks. Design the lettering using one of the methods in Fig. 3:5 to show one of the following:
(a) DEAN LTD;
(b) TENKA;
(c) TRIDENT;
(d) HONDA;
(e) FORD.

3:6

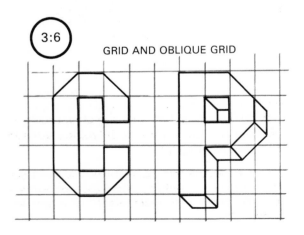

GRID AND OBLIQUE GRID

Q6 Use the grid system shown in Fig. 3:6 to design the letters and numbers on a personalised number plate for your motor bike. The minimum number of digits is six. Provide your own back plate and show where the holes needed for bolting it onto the frame will be placed.

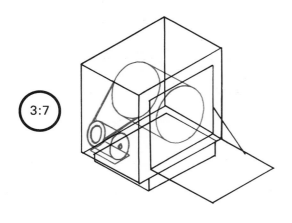

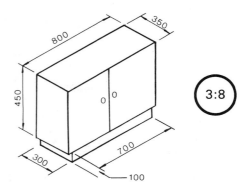

Transparent Pictorial Views

Figure 3:7 shows a tumble-drier in **transparent pictorial view.**

Q7 Draw the sideboard unit in Fig. 3:8 to a suitable scale in transparent pictorial view. Include in your drawing (a) an internal central vertical partition; (b) a shelf on centre in the left-hand space; (c) two shelves in the right-hand space.

Graphic Action Printing

The styles of printing in Fig. 3:9 attempt to show broken glass and leaking fluid. As an advertisement they also attract attention to the services offered.

Q8 Design the lettering for a tubular steel manufacturer providing round and rectangular tubing whose trading name is CLAREN.

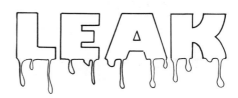

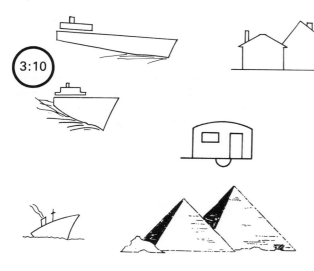

Shapes in Outline

Commodities offered for sale are often shown as outlines which aim to present the basic shapes to the public (see Fig. 3:10).

Q9 Use an **outline technique** to indicate the goods sold by a do-it-yourself shop whose *main* service is supplying tools and materials to the amateur woodworker.

USING LINES

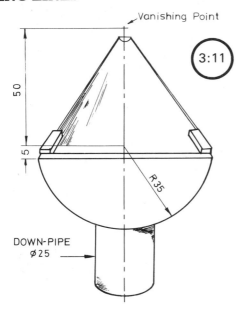

Vanishing Point

3:11

50

5

R 35

DOWN-PIPE
Ø 25

Distance Lines (Perspective)

Q10 Draw the rain gutter shown in Fig. 3:11 and supply colour or texture to indicate its shape.

Optical Illusions

The lines in Fig. 3:12 can be interpreted as rays of outward energy or as running inwards to a distant hole.

Q11 Using an arc or circle of diameter 90 mm draw the view seen looking into a road or rail tunnel.

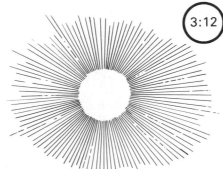

OPTICAL ILLUSION LINES

3:12

1. RAYS OF OUTWARD ENERGY
2. DISTANT HOLE - INWARD

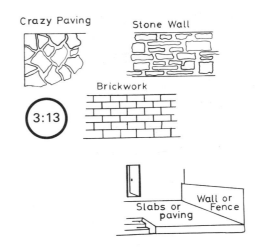

Crazy Paving   Stone Wall

Brickwork

3:13

Slabs or
paving

Wall or
Fence

Textures of Building Materials

Q12 (a) Design and draw a decorative brick or paved surface 45 mm high and 100 mm long. (b) Draw part of a back garden in pictorial form showing a paved area 100 m × 80 m and a wall (Fig. 3:13).

Q13 Use the dimensions given in Fig. 3:14 to draw a pictorial view of a garden. Add a door and window, and show textures on the surfaces.

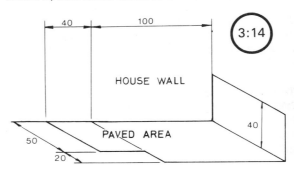

40   100

3:14

HOUSE WALL

50

PAVED AREA

40

20

Soft texture

Figure 3:15 shows a Perspex spoon on which the soft sheen has been indicated.

Q14 Using instruments, draw a pictorial view of a record player. Indicate by texture the materials in (a) the Perspex top; (b) the wooden box frame; (c) a turntable made of a named material of your choice.

3:15

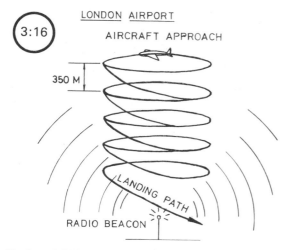

3:16

LONDON AIRPORT

AIRCRAFT APPROACH

350 M

LANDING PATH

RADIO BEACON

Paths of Objects

Figure 3:16 shows the path taken by an aircraft coming down to land at London Airport.

Q15 A fairground has a variety of rides for the customers to enjoy. Use a line method to show one of the more exciting rides to be found there.

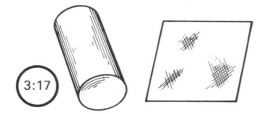

3:17

To Indicate Shape

Q16 Draw a chimney stack with two chimney pots in pictorial form. Use a texture technique like that in Fig. 3:17 to indicate the earthenware pots and the brickwork.

To Show Material

Q17 Using the techniques shown in Fig. 3:18, design a leaflet suitable as an advertisement for a window fitter.

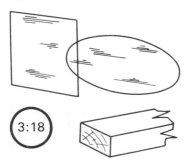

3:18

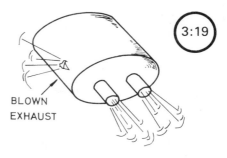

3:19

BLOWN
EXHAUST

To Indicate Movement

In Fig. 3:19, lines have been used to show the gases coming out of the exhaust pipes of a car.

Q18 Draw an advertisement for a 24-hour plumbing service that caters mainly for emergency services.

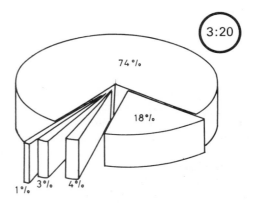

3:20

74%

18%

1%   3%   4%

Three-dimensional Pie Charts

Q19 Choose an evening's television programmes and split them into separate sections, e.g. news, comedy, etc. Produce a pie chart like that in Fig. 3:20 to compare the time given to each type.

3:21

Silhouettes

Q20 Use the silhouette method shown in Fig. 3:21 to design a pictogram indicating the key cutter's trade for his headed note paper.

4 Flow Charts

Symbols

The symbols shown here for use in flow charts have been taken from BS 4058:1973, which includes all data-processing symbols including computer use and management.

The flow chart shown in Fig. 4:1 shows the main processes involved at meal times.

Q1 Copy the chart, making the symbols 50 mm wide and of a suitable height.

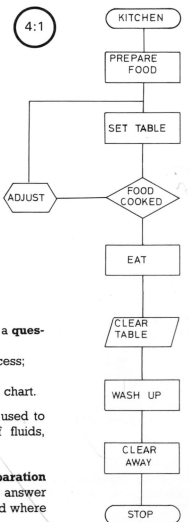

Start, restart, halt/interrupt, fault, stop.

This symbol represents a **general process** without stating the method or equipment used. It serves the general progression without
(a) problem solving;
(b) extra equipment;
(c) introducing any changes.

This symbol indicates a **decision** or a **question** and is included where there is
(a) the need to test or check a process;
(b) an alternative process;
(c) a question arising from the flow chart.

The symbol for **input** or **output** is used to show the addition or removal of fluids, materials, equipment, etc.

Changes, Alternatives, Extra Preparation
This symbol normally follows a NO answer from a decision point. It is also found where alterations are required.

Lines

A **flow line** joins symbols. Arrows may be added to indicate the direction of flow.

The **junctions** of flow lines should be spaced well apart. Flow lines should not cross at a junction.

A **broken line** leads to explanatory notes that clarify a situation. The flow chart stops at this point, although suggested remedies may be indicated.

An electrical appliance suddenly stops working and you suspect that a fuse has blown. The flow chart in Fig. 4:2 describes the main processes involved in replacing ceramic fuses in the more usual 3–13 amp range.

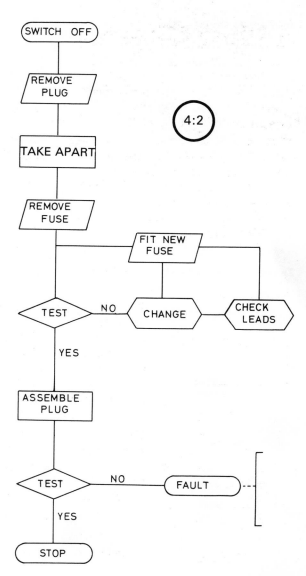

Q2 Copy the flow chart in Fig. 4:2 and insert any arrows that you feel are needed.

Insert possible faults in the appropriate place.

Q3 A copper bedside lamp that will not light has an insulated bulb fitting and a switch on the cable, *not* on the lamp base. The power is supplied by a 3-pin plug from the mains and the lamp is earthed by a screw in its base.

The cause of the fault could be (a) broken bulb; (b) blown fuse; (c) faulty plug connection; (d) broken switch.

Draw a flow chart to show how you would trace the fault, presuming that the switch was broken and that you checked the items in the order given above.

Q4 Produce a flow chart to show the sequence of tasks involved in repainting a badly weathered door.
The following processes are involved:
(a) burning off old paint, checking smooth surface, filling holes;
(b) scraping down with wire brush;
(c) smoothing down;
(d) priming with primer paint;
(e) checking that it is dry and rubbing down to remove any unevenness;
(f) applying undercoat;
(g) leaving it to dry;
(h) applying gloss coat.

To avoid an extra-long flow chart, items such as undoing the screws have been included in the main processes.

43

PROGRESS FLOW CHARTS

Whenever an idea or a set of information has to be presented, various thought processes have to be followed to determine the design of the graphic base. One convenient method is to use the progress flow chart shown in Fig. 4:3. In this case the method has been applied to designing ideograms, but it could equally well be adapted to other problems.

Q5 Produce a similar flow chart for one of the following activities:
(a) the things you do from rising in the morning until you leave home for school;
(b) setting up a rod and line for float fishing;
(c) preparing for a weekend away from home.

Designing Ideograms

Actions

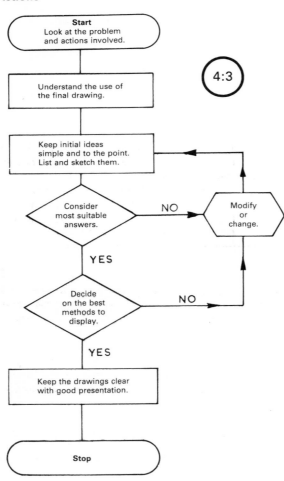

Problems

Understand the use of the pictogram, e.g. for information, display, warning, emergency, direction, etc.

Keep the topics and any other associated ideas in your mind whilst sketching and planning your solution.

Some answers may indicate something other than you intended. Look at your solutions and check back to the first process.

Various outline shapes indicate different degrees of importance, e.g. a triangle is usually a warning sign. Your ideogram must completely satisfy the problem.

Decide where and how much colour should be used. Choose a size that is suitable for the ideogram's use.

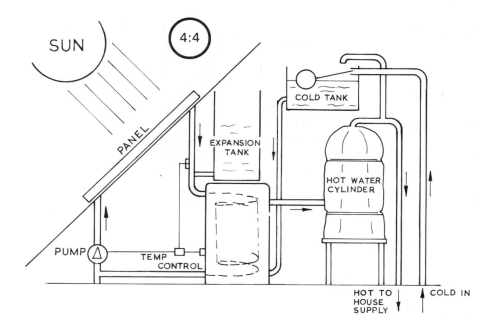

SUN

4:4

PANEL

EXPANSION TANK

COLD TANK

HOT WATER CYLINDER

PUMP

TEMP CONTROL

HOT TO HOUSE SUPPLY

COLD IN

Q6 Follow the water flow in the solar heater in Fig. 4:4 and produce a flow chart that shows the movement of the water from the cold supply to the hot water cylinder.
1 **Read** the names of the parts.
2 **Understand** the flow.
3 **Draw** the flow chart.

Q7 Produce a flow chart to show how a colour film is processed. The following stages are used:
First development in tank—drain off developer—add stop bath, then drain off—wash film—take out of tank and expose to bright floodlight—add colour developer—add stop bath, then drain off—wash film—add bleaching liquid, then drain off—wash film—add fixative, then drain off—wash film—harden (stabilize).

Q8 A new electric appliance has been supplied without a plug. Show by means of a flow chart how the cable with the earth wire, live wire and neutral wire is fitted to a plug and tested.

Q9 The gear chain on your bicycle has broken and you have to repair and replace it by going through the following processes:
Remove chain—remove broken link—clean the chain with paraffin (add process)—insert new link—undo rear wheel—fit chain—replace rear wheel—realign wheel—check tension—oil chain.
Construct a flow chart to show this.

Q10 You are about to start a new engineering drawing in the graphics office. Produce a flow chart to show the processes you go through when bordering and printing in your paper, prior to drawing.

Q11 The brake blocks on your bicycle need replacing. List the processes you would need to follow to replace them and use these processes to produce a flow chart.

Q12 The family car needs its spark plugs replaced. Show by means of a flow chart how the new plugs are fitted in place of the old ones and how they are set prior to fitting.

5 Workshop Drawings

ORTHOGRAPHIC PROJECTION

The methods of drawing studied so far, **freehand perspective**, and **isometric** and **oblique projections**, are all most useful when presenting an overall picture of an easily recognisable object. But if the intention is to go beyond recognition and to indicate how to make the object, then accurate measurements are needed for every line shown in the drawing. This usually calls for a separate drawing of each face of the object with a means of linking the drawings in the proper order.

The technique known as **orthographic projection** is used to achieve these drawings. It is helpful to regard orthographic projections as **workshop drawings**.

If an object is placed behind a vertical sheet of glass (A in Fig. 5:1), lines can be drawn on the glass which correspond to the edges of the object. This produces a **front view**, also called an **elevation**, of the object, with every line in the drawing the same length as the corresponding line on the object.

This procedure can be repeated with the vertical plane at B to produce a **side elevation**, and again with a horizontal plane at C to produce a **plan view**.

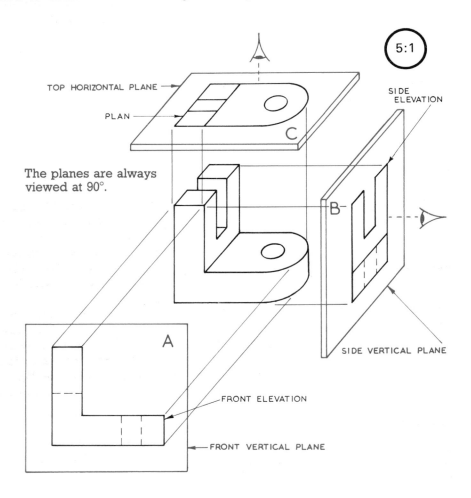

The planes are always viewed at 90°.

TOP HORIZONTAL PLANE

PLAN

SIDE ELEVATION

5:1

SIDE VERTICAL PLANE

FRONT ELEVATION

FRONT VERTICAL PLANE

When the adjoining edges of the glass sheets A, B and C are linked up as shown, a three-sided right-angled corner is produced.

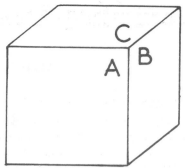

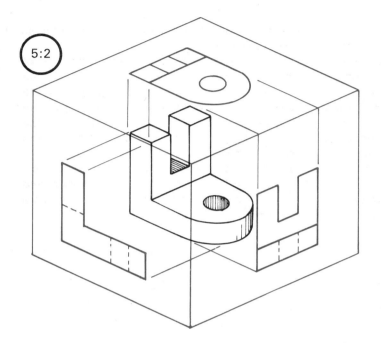

5:2

If the object is then placed centrally behind this corner, it can be looked at through each of the three glass sheets in turn. The three views will be seen in the positions shown in Fig. 5:2.

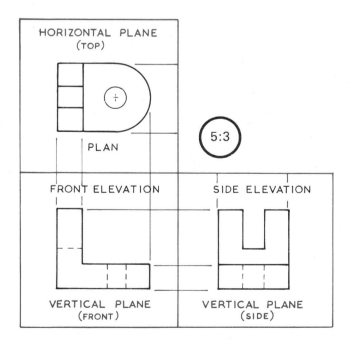

5:3

The joints between the planes can then be used as hinges and the planes opened out as shown in Fig. 5:3. This produces a workshop drawing which has each line of the exact length. The full title of this drawing is **third angle orthographic projection**.

The three views shown in Fig. 5:3 are the ones most commonly used. If necessary a second side view, looking from the left of the object, can be added. This view will be placed to the left of the front vertical plane on the workshop drawing.

Terms to remember are:
  plan,
  front elevation,
  side or end elevation.

47

If the front vertical plane (**VP**) and the horizontal plane (**HP**) are placed together, their lengths can be extended to divide space into four 90° dihedral angles. For drawing purposes these are called, moving anti-clockwise, the **first, second, third** and **fourth angles**. Each one of these angles can be used as a base to contain the object to be drawn. A few years ago first angle drawings were the most common (Fig. 5:6) but nowadays third angle projections (Fig. 5:15) are the standard method for producing workshop drawings, and are used in this book unless otherwise stated.

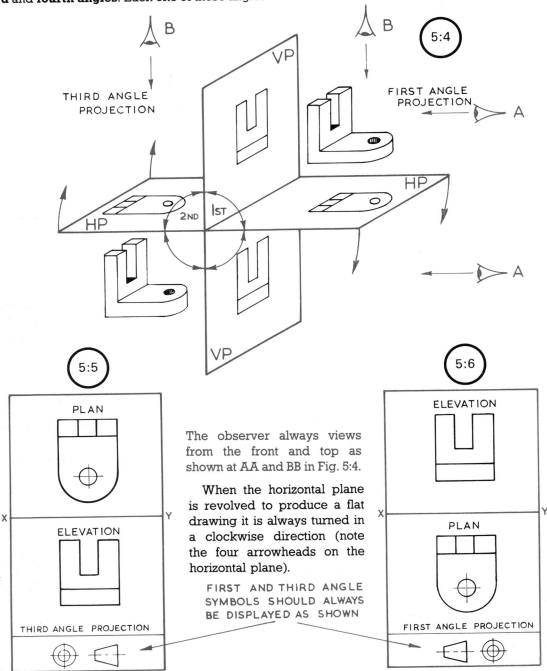

The observer always views from the front and top as shown at AA and BB in Fig. 5:4.

When the horizontal plane is revolved to produce a flat drawing it is always turned in a clockwise direction (note the four arrowheads on the horizontal plane).

FIRST AND THIRD ANGLE SYMBOLS SHOULD ALWAYS BE DISPLAYED AS SHOWN

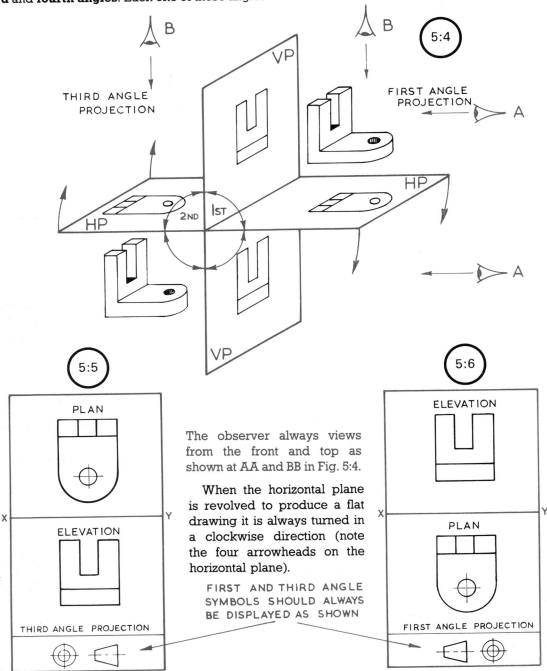 labels: THIRD ANGLE PROJECTION / FIRST ANGLE PROJECTION / VP / HP / HP / VP / 2ND / 1ST / A / A / B / B / 5:4 / 5:5 / PLAN / ELEVATION / X / Y / THIRD ANGLE PROJECTION / 5:6 / ELEVATION / PLAN / X / Y / FIRST ANGLE PROJECTION

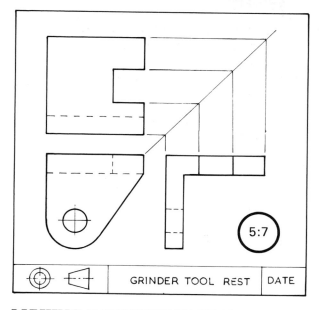

GRINDER TOOL REST | DATE

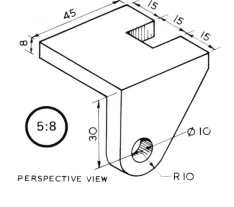

GRINDER TOOL REST

5:8 PERSPECTIVE VIEW

MAKING A WORKSHOP DRAWING

Figure 5:7 shows a third angle projection (workshop drawing) of a grinding machine tool rest. Figure 5:8 shows a perspective view of the same object.

To make a third angle projection of the tool rest.

1 Decide which viewpoint will produce the clearest front elevation.

2 Add the length of the front view to the width of the side view, and allow about 30 mm for the gap between the views. This total gives the overall length AB of the finished drawing (see Fig. 5:9). In the same way add 30 mm to the combined height of the front view and the width of the plan to obtain the overall height of the drawing (AC).

3 Draw these main construction lines very thin and faint.

4 In the corner of this right angle set out in thin line the overall shape of the front elevation (Fig. 5:10).

5 From this front elevation project the overall shape of the plan, leaving a 30 mm gap between the two views (Fig. 5:10).

6 Draw a thin 45° line from the top right-hand corner of the front elevation. This makes easier the transfer of dimensions from the plan to the end elevation.

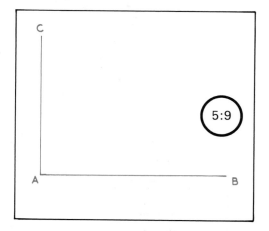

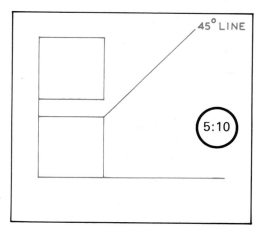

7 Project a continuation of the two lines that mark the height of the front elevation, and so establish the overall height of the end elevation (Fig. 5:11). Project the overall dimension lines from the plan, first horizontally across to the 45° line and then vertically down to cut the two lines projected from the front elevation. This establishes the overall shape of the end elevation.

Note that the outline of this third view has been obtained by projection only, and not by further measuring.

When the object being drawn contains circles or circular arcs the centre-lines for these are drawn first, then the circles and arcs, and the straight connecting lines last of all. This method is used because it is much easier to draw a straight line so that it blends smoothly with a curve than to draw an arc or circle to run smoothly into a straight line.

8 Carefully measure and mark in the centre-lines and draw the circle in full line and the arc in faint line (Fig. 5:12). The arc is drawn over in full line after faint straight lines have been drawn to mark its limits.

9 Add the remaining details, taking great care to blend the straight lines into the arc.

10 Erase all construction lines except the two centre-lines in the circle.

11 Make sure that all the views have firm and solid yet clear and sharp outlines (Fig. 5:13).

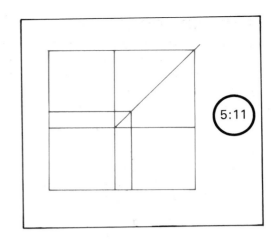

5:11

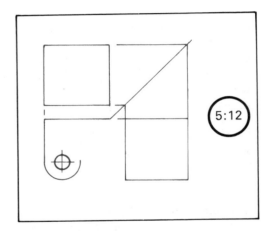

5:12

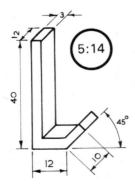

5:14

Q1 Draw twice full size in third angle projection a front elevation, end elevation and plan of the towel hook in Fig. 5:14.

Q2 Make another three-view workshop drawing of the towel hook, twice full size, in first angle projection.

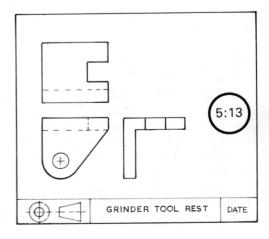

5:13

GRINDER TOOL REST | DATE

LINES AND DIMENSIONS

Lines can have differences in thickness, intensity and intensity, Constant usage over many years has produced a general agreement on a standard practice whereby these lines can be made to represent different features of an object.

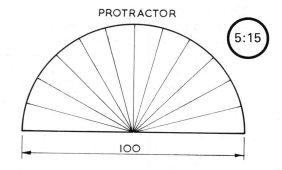

PROTRACTOR

5:15

The Outline

This gives an object its shape and should, therefore, be uniformly black and dense to make reading the drawing easier.

Q3 Copy the drawing of the protractor (Fig. 5:15). Try to make all the lines of exactly the same width and density.

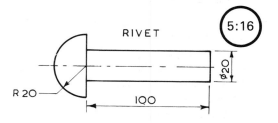

RIVET

5:16

The Centre-line

Centre-lines are always thin chain lines made up of long and short dashes. They always start and finish with a long dash and extend for a short distance beyond the outline. When two centre-lines intersect, e.g. at the centre of a circle, they always cross on the long dashes.

Q4 Copy the drawings of the rivet (Fig. 5:16) and the split washer (Fig. 5:17). Show clearly the differences in width between the outlines and the centre-lines.

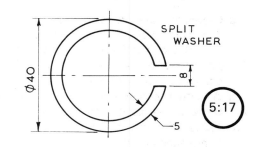

SPLIT WASHER

5:17

Dimension and Projection Lines

The protractor, rivet and washer in the diagrams can all be readily visualised from the outlines given. By themselves, however, the outlines do not provide the whole picture. In each case dimensions are needed to give the actual size of each object. Dimension lines are therefore of equal importance to the outlines in showing the true shape and size of an object.

Both projection and dimension lines are thin and continuous. Whenever possible they are drawn outside the outline of the object. Projection lines start about 2 mm clear of the outline and extend the same distance beyond the arrowheads at the end of the dimension lines. These arrowheads should touch the projection lines.

Figures to indicate actual sizes are placed at right-angles to the dimension lines, reading from the bottom and the right-hand side of the drawing.

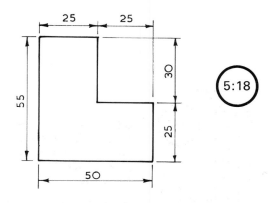

5:18

Q5 Copy to full size the template shown in Fig. 5:18. Insert all the dimensions. Take special care to keep the arrowheads thin and neat.

Lines and Their Uses

Types of lines	Thickness in mm	Uses of lines	Detail no.
Continuous bold	0.7	Outlines and edges that are visible	1
Continuous thin	0.3	Dimension lines Leader lines Projection lines Hatching Outline of revolved sections	2 3 4 5 6
Short dashes thin	0.3	Hidden detail and edges	7
Chain thin	0.3	Centre-lines Centre points of circles Extreme position of moving parts	8 9 10
Continuous irregular thin	0.3	Marking the limit of a partial section (when it does not coincide with an axis)	11
	0.3	Interrupted lengths of shafts and rods	12
Chain	0.7 and 0.3	Cutting planes (0.7 mm at the ends and at changes of direction; 0.3 mm elsewhere)	13
	0.3	Square on a shaft	14

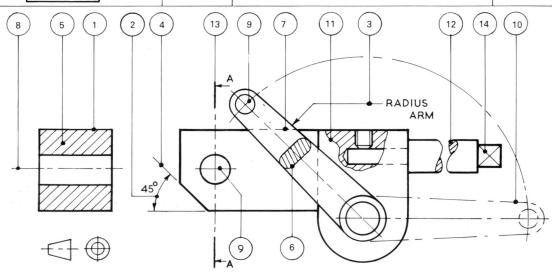

Dimensioning Holes

Holes are positioned by marking out their centre point at a given distance from an edge.

Dimension lines drawn across circles must not coincide with the centre-lines. They are best drawn at 45°. A leader line can then carry the dimension figure clear of the drawing, as with the ∅ 30 in Fig. 5:19.

∅ is an agreed symbol for the word 'diameter' and *R* is an abbrevation of 'radius'. These symbols are always placed **before** the dimension figures.

A centre-line is never used as a dimension line, but it can be extended and the extension used for dimensioning.

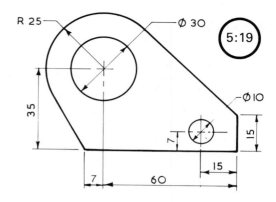

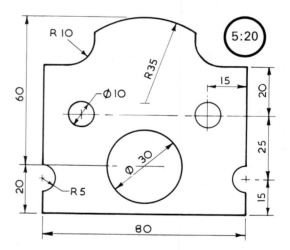

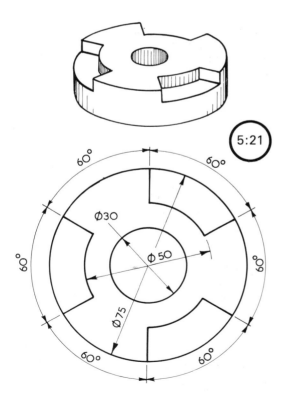

Q6 Draw the Yale-type backplate in Fig. 5:20 to the sizes given. Start with the centre-lines for the large circle. Dimension the drawing as shown.

Q7 Copy the plan view of the lawn mower clutch plate (Fig. 5:21) to the sizes given. Start with the centre-lines.

Make sure that the circles and arcs are of the same intensity as the straight lines.

SECTIONS

Section Lines and Hidden Details

A problem constantly facing draughtsmen is how to clearly show details that are hidden inside an object. The agreed method is to indicate hidden details by means of short, thin dash lines. In Fig. 5:22 the use of these clearly indicates the position of the clapper and also shows the gradual thinning of the bell wall.

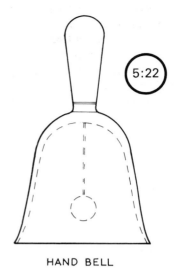

HAND BELL

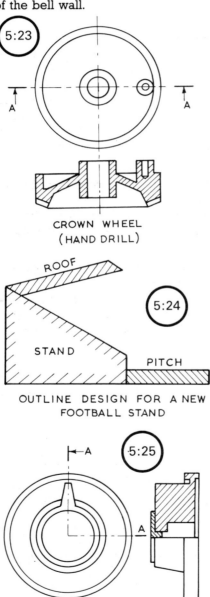

CROWN WHEEL
(HAND DRILL)

OUTLINE DESIGN FOR A NEW
FOOTBALL STAND

GAS COOKER CONTROL

Full Cross-sections

When the number of hidden detail lines could make the drawing confusing it is customary to draw a sectional view. This is obtained by imagining that the object has been sliced through by a cutting plane and the front portion removed to reveal the hidden details (see Fig. 5:23). The cut surface is drawn covered with oblique lines rather like the scratches left by saw teeth. These lines are called **section lines**, and the face is said to have been **cross-hatched**.

Section lines are drawn at 45° to the main edges of the face and incline the same way in every view of that item. Section lines on adjacent parts slope in opposite directions. The distance between the lines can be varied when there are more than two items. Large areas need only have cross-hatching around the edges (see Fig. 5:24).

Half-sections

Objects that are symmetrical about their axis can be drawn in half-section as shown in Fig. 5:25. This method presents one half of the item in section and the other in full outline.

The part that is cut away is shown removed only in the sectional view and not in any of the other views.

Revolved Sections and Removed Sections

Elongated objects of comparatively small cross-section can have their thickness indicated by means of a **revolved section**, where the imaginary section plane is revolved through 90°. This is shown on the spanner handle in Fig. 5:26.

Alternatively, shape and thickness can be clearly shown by removing the cross-section and drawing it adjacent to the object, as in Fig. 5:27.

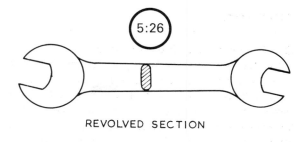

REVOLVED SECTION

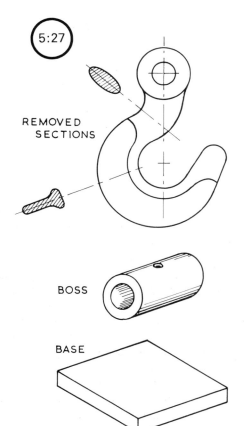

REMOVED SECTIONS

BOSS

BASE

BOSS

RIB

5:28

SUPPORT   BASE

Cross-sections In Use

Two related design problems that are common to most kinds of machines are how to provide support for a revolving shaft or spindle while at the same time maintaining the exact position of the shaft in relation to adjacent parts of the machine. The solution to these two requirements consists of three essential parts:

1 A boss to hold the shaft.
2 A suitably shaped base for fixing to the machine frame.
3 A support stand and ribs to join the boss to the base and to keep them at the specified distance apart.

Figure 5:28 shows a typical example of such a shaft support bracket.

Figure 5:29 shows a centre-line cross-section through the bracket and includes a short length of the shaft. Note the method used to show a shaft of unknown length.

When a cutting plane sections a rib longitudinally it is always shown solid and never cross-hatched.

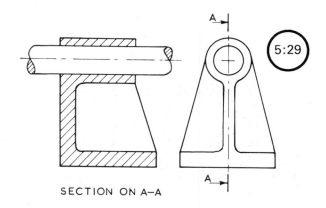

SECTION ON A–A

55

Part Sections

Small hidden details can be shown by means of a part section. Figure 5:30 shows a key seating in the end of a spindle. Note the irregular boundary line to the section.

Figure 5:31 shows a complete centre-line cross-section of a support tube housing a ball race bearing. This carries a shaft on which a gear wheel is secured by means of a key, nut and washer.

When a section plane cuts longitudinally through standard parts, such as shafts, nuts, bolts, washers, screws, rivets, ball and roller bearings and gear teeth, it is normal practice not to show these cross-hatched.

EXERCISES ON SECTION DRAWINGS

Exercises may be drawn in either 1st or 3rd angle projection.

Q8 Copy the elevation of a multi-layer eraser given in Fig. 5:32. Add the end elevation and on this latter insert cross-hatching lines (Section A–A).

Q9 Copy the plan of the chipboard joint block in Fig. 5:33 to twice full size. From this plan project a centre-line cross-sectioned elevation on the cutting plane A–A.

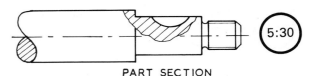

PART SECTION

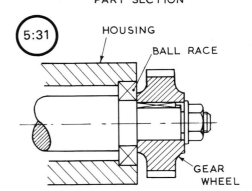

HOUSING

BALL RACE

GEAR WHEEL

FULL CENTRELINE SECTION

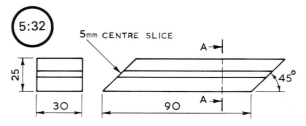

5mm CENTRE SLICE

Q10 Figure 5:34 shows a standard machine clamp such as are in common use for fastening castings to drilling and milling machine tables for machining operations.

Draw the following views:

(a) A centre-line cross-sectional elevation from A.
(b) An end elevation looking from B.
(c) A plan view.

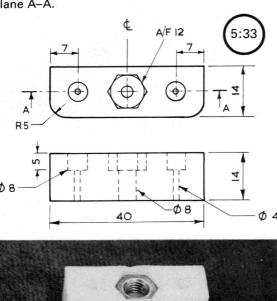

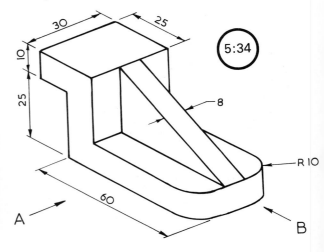

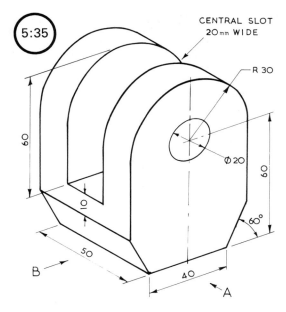

CENTRAL SLOT
20mm WIDE

5:35

R 30

Ø 20

60

60

60

50

40

B

A

60°

10

Q11 Figure 5:35 gives details of a universal coupling head. Draw the following views:
(a) A front elevation looking from A.
(b) An end elevation looking from B.
(c) A plan view.
Insert all the dimensions in each case.

Q12 The details of a bench stop which can be used on portable woodwork benches are given in Fig. 5:36. The locating peg is centrally placed in the rectangle. Draw the following views:
(a) An elevation looking from A.
(b) An end elevation.
(c) A plan. Show hidden detail and dimension this view.

Q13 Figure 5:37 gives details of a grinding machine tool rest. Draw the following views:
(a) An elevation looking from the direction A.
(b) An end elevation looking from B.
(c) A plan. Dimension the outline of this plan.

Q14 The dimensions of the soap holder shown in the photograph are given in Fig. 5:38.
Draw the following views:
(a) A front elevation viewed from A.
(b) A plan projected from (a) above. Include hidden detail in the plan.
(c) An end elevation.

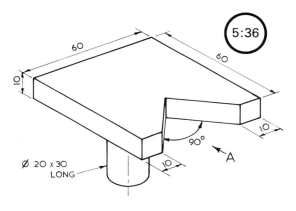

5:36

60

60

10

10

10

90°

A

Ø 20 x 30
LONG

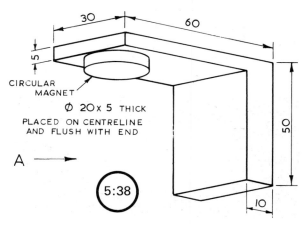

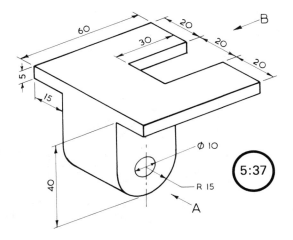

60

30

20

20

20

B

5

15

40

Ø 10

R 15

A

5:37

30

60

5

CIRCULAR
MAGNET

Ø 20 x 5 THICK

PLACED ON CENTRELINE
AND FLUSH WITH END

A

50

10

5:38

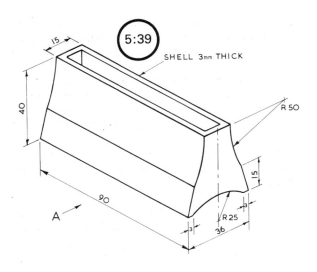

5:39

SHELL 3mm THICK

R 50

15

R 25

R 25

40

90

A

15

3

3

36

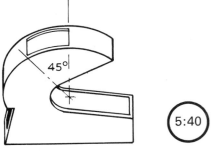

45°

5:40

Q15 A plastic hair-dryer nozzle is shown in Fig. 5:39. Draw the following views twice full size:
(a) An elevation looking along arrow A.
(b) A plan projected from the view in (a).
(e) An end elevation.

Q16 The dimensions of the Dymo cartridge case in the photograph are given in Fig. 5:40.
Draw the following twice full size:
(a) Copy the given elevation.
(b) Project a plan from the elevation.
(c) Draw both end elevations.
The wall thickness is 1 mm throughout.

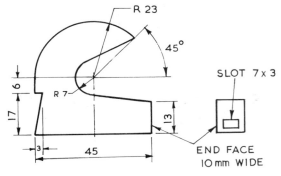

R 23

45°

SLOT 7 x 3

6

R 7

17

13

3

45

END FACE
10 mm WIDE

Q17 Figure 5:41 gives detailed dimensions of the shelf bracket shown in the photograph.
Draw the following views full size:
(a) A front elevation.
(b) A plan projected from the view in (a).
(c) Both end elevations.

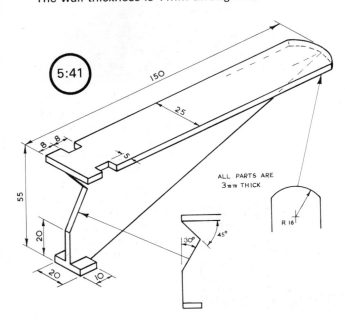

5:41

150

25

8 8

5

55

ALL PARTS ARE
3mm THICK

R 16

20

30°

45°

20

10

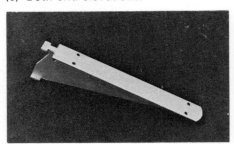

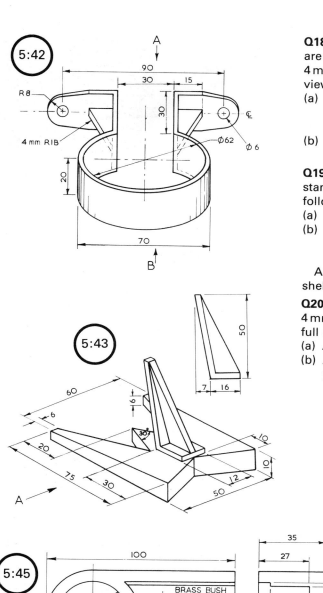

Q18 The dimensions of a rainwater downpipe clip are given in Fig. 5:42. The clip is moulded from 4 mm thick polypropylene. Draw the following views:

(a) A sectional plan looking from A. The section should be taken along the horizontal centre-line, thus cutting the ribs longitudinally.

(b) An elevation looking from B. Show all hidden detail in this view.

Q19 Figure 5:43 gives the basic dimensions for a stand suitable for a model aeroplane. Draw the following views:

(a) A plan.

(b) A centre-line cross-sectional elevation projected from the plan and looking in the direction of the arrow A.

All the material is 3 mm thick, and the base is a shell, it is not solid.

Q20 Figure 5:44 gives detailed dimensions for a 4 mm thick gutter clip. Draw the following views full size:

(a) A front elevation looking from A.

(b) A centre-line cross-sectioned and elevation projected from the view in (a).

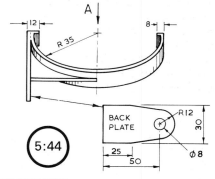

Q21 Dimensioned details of the two parts A and B that make up the shower tube guide are given in Fig. 5:45. Draw the following views of the assembled guide:

(a) An elevation with the guide in the same position as the body A.

(b) A longitudinal centre-line cross-section projected from the view in (a).

59

FILLETS

When objects are produced by a casting process, molten metal or plastic is poured or injected into a suitably shaped mould. As the molten material cools it also contracts slightly. This contraction produces strains inside the casting, particularly where there is an abrupt change of shape, e.g. on internal angles. To prevent the strain from producing a crack in the material, these corners are strengthened with a curved filling called a **fillet**.

Fillets are usually shown on drawings with a radius of about 5 mm and are indicated on sketches by three faint lines (see Fig. 4:46).

Drawing Fillet Arcs

The centre of the arc that represents the fillet is situated at the intersection of the lines which are drawn parallel to the outlines and the fillet radius away from them, as shown in Fig. 5:47.

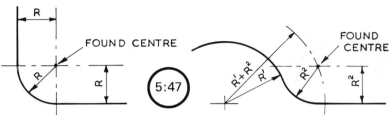

Q22 Figure 5:48 is a sketch of a plumber's pipe clip. Draw and dimension the following views:
(a) A plan.
(b) A front elevation projected from the plan.
(c) An end elevation viewed from the right.

Q23 Draw the following views of the gear change fork shown in Fig. 5:49:
(a) A front elevation looking from A.
(b) A plan projected from the view in (a).
(c) An end elevation looking from B.

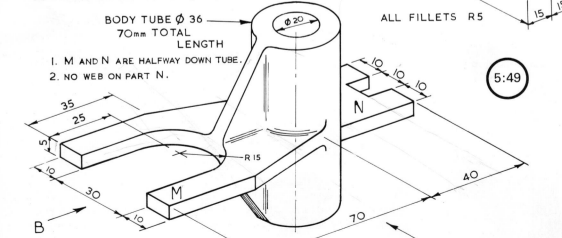

60

JOINING CURVES

Two arcs may be joined by a concave curve, as in Fig. 5:50, or by a convex curve, as in Fig. 5:51.

To Join Two Arcs with a Concave Arc of Radius *R*
(Fig. 5:50)

1 From the centre of the larger circle draw an arc of radius $R + R_1$.
2 From the centre of the smaller circle draw an arc of radius $R + R_2$.
3 These two arcs intersect in the centre of the blending circle.

To Join Two Arcs with a Convex Arc of Radius *R*
(Fig. 5:51)

1 From the centre of the larger circle draw an arc of radius $R - R_1$.
2 From the centre of the smaller circle draw an arc of radius $R - R_2$.
3 These two arcs intersect at the centre of the blending circle.

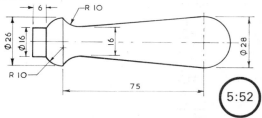

Q24 The outline dimensions of an engineer's file handle are given in Fig. 5:52. Copy the drawing to full size.

Q25 The profile and dimensions of a plane handle like those fitted to the front of iron woodworking planes are shown in Fig. 5:53. Copy the outline and include all the dimensions.

Q26 Figure 5:54 gives the dimensions of a scalpel blade. Copy the outline twice full size.

Q27 Figure 5:55 shows the rear handle of a woodworking plane. Copy the profile and add the dimensions.

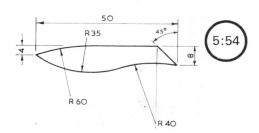

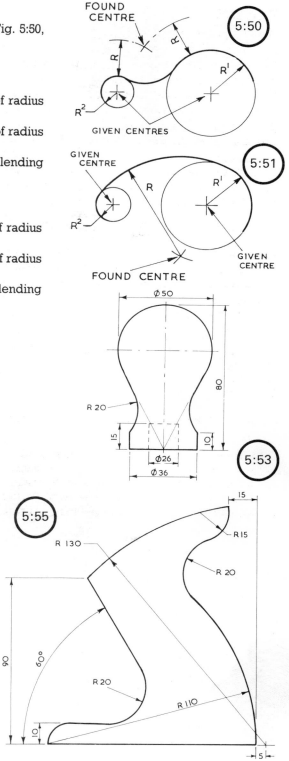

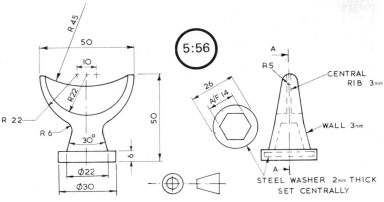

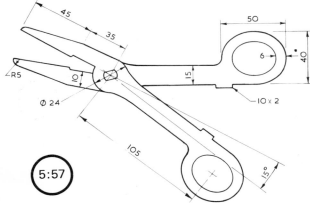

Q28 Figure 5:56 details all the dimensions of the football stud key in the photograph. Draw twice full size a centre-line cross-sectional elevation looking in the direction A–A.

Q29 Figure 5:57 gives details of a type of plastic disposable tongs used daily in clinics and hospitals. Draw the outline of one leg only, using your judgement for any dimensions not shown.

Q30 Figure 5:58 shows detailed elevations of the electric blow-dry comb in the photograph. Copy the two elevations and add five teeth in the left-hand space. All teeth should be 2 mm thick.

Q31 The plan view of a water tap is shown in Fig. 5:59. Copy the given view, taking care to blend the various arcs into a smooth curved outline.

To locate point A add the two radii (10 + 25) to give a combined radius of 35 mm. Using this radius and centres B and C, draw the two intersecting arcs at A.

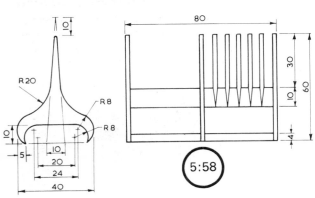

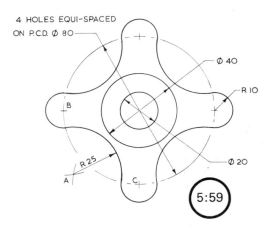

Q32 Draw the following views of the trolley castor fork in Fig. 5:60 to full size:
(a) A front elevation looking from A.
(b) A plan projected from the view in (a).
(c) A side elevation looking from B.
Add your own design of a wheel and its shaft to all views. Include a means of securing the shaft in the fork.

Q33 The photograph and drawing (Fig. 5:61) give details of a protractor saw guide as fitted to many small portable circular saws. Draw full size the following views:
(a) A plan looking from A with the 20 mm fence parallel with the vertical plane.
(b) A front elevation projected from the view in (a).
(c) An end elevation sectioned through the 90° graduation and the centre hole.
    Show an M8 hexagonal nut and washer in place of the wing nut in the photograph (A/C 16.0). The base is 5 mm thick, as shown in the part section.

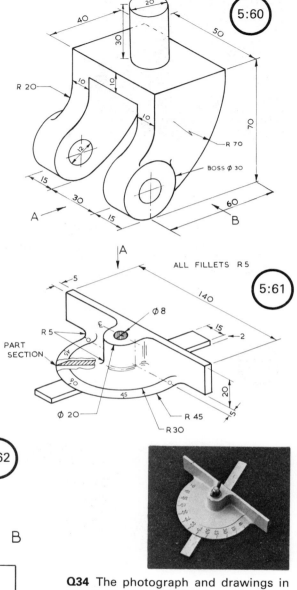

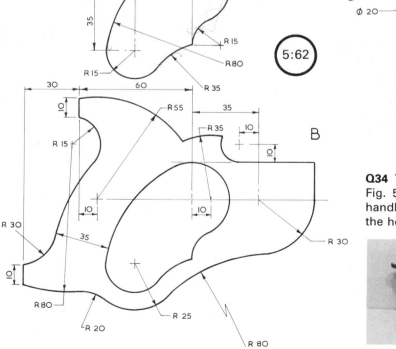

Q34 The photograph and drawings in Fig. 5:62 give details of a tenon saw handle. Copy it, full size, starting with the hole detailed in drawing A.

63

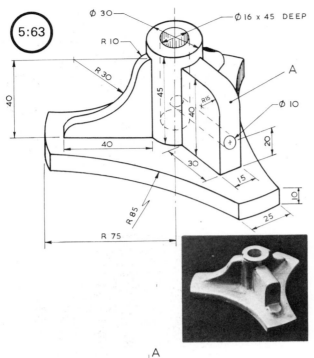

5:63

∅ 30
∅ 16 x 45 DEEP
R 10
R 30
A
40
45
R 15
∅ 10
40
7·40
30
20
15
R 85
25
10
R 75

Q35 Figure 5:63 gives dimensions similar to those of the aluminium sprinkler base shown in the photograph. Draw the following views full size, taking details from the sketch:
(a) A plan with the rib A along the horizontal centre-line.
(b) A front elevation projected from the view in (a).
(c) A centre-line cross-sectioned end elevation.

Q36 Figure 5:64 shows a half-sectioned sketch of a fuse holder which consists of four parts: two brass contacts, one ceramic core, one plastic body. Draw, twice full size, the following views of the assembled fuse:
(a) A plan view looking from A.
(b) A front elevation projected from the plan and cross-sectioned longitudinally through the 3 mm diameter wire channel.

Q37 A half-sectioned view of a stuffing gland of a type widely used on motor boat propeller shafts is shown in Fig. 5:65. Draw, full size, the following views:
(a) A centre-line cross-sectioned elevation looking along arrow A.
(b) An end elevation looking from the left.
(c) A plan view.

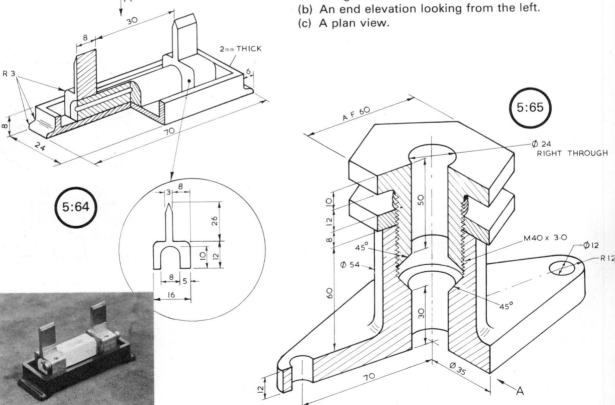

A
30
8
2mm THICK
R 3
6
8
70
24

5:64

3
8
26
10
12
8
5
16

5:65

A F 60
∅ 24
RIGHT THROUGH
10
12
50
8
45°
M40 x 3·0
∅ 12
R 12
∅ 54
45°
60
30
12
70
∅ 35
A

Q38 The photograph shows a flat-crowned car piston complete with its gudgeon pin. The piston has been sawn in half to give a centre-line cross-sectional view. Figure 5:66 shows a domed two-stroke motor cycle piston which has been cut to present a half-sectioned view.

Draw the following views:
(a) A front elevation looking from A.
(b) An end elevation with the right-hand half shown in section and the left-hand half shown in outline.

Q39 Figure 5:67 details the parts needed to make up the kitchen mandolin (for slicing vegetables thinly) shown in the photograph.
(a) Copy the drawing of the handle, B, and add the remaining parts to form a complete front view.
(b) Draw a cross-sectioned view along the longitudinal centre-line.

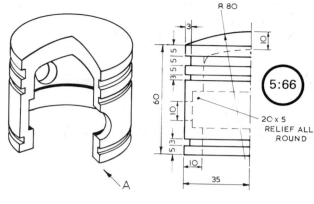

5:66

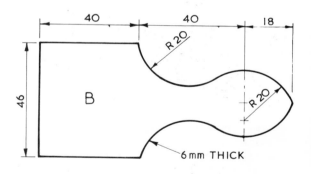

SIDES PINNED TO 'B' AND 'C' ON ℄

5:67

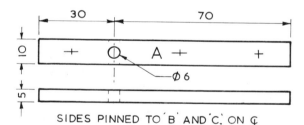

B

6 mm THICK

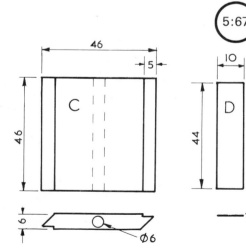

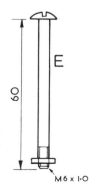

E

M6 x 1·0

PARTS LIST

	ITEM	REQD	MATL
A	SIDES	2	WOOD
B	HANDLE	1	WOOD
C	BLOCK	1	WOOD
D	CUTTERS	2	CARBON STEEL
E	BOLT	1	MILD STEEL

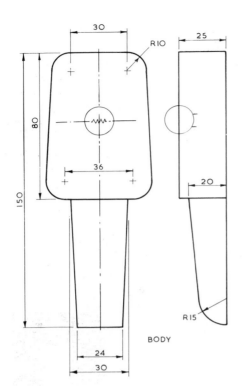

BODY

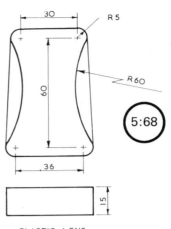

PLASTIC LENS

THE BODY AND LENS ARE
BOTH HOLLOW AND HAVE
WALLS 3mm THICK

5:68

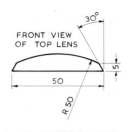

FRONT VIEW
OF TOP LENS

5:69

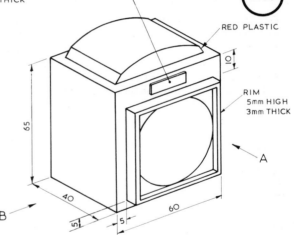

PRESS SWITCH 20 X 6 X 2

RED PLASTIC

RIM
5mm HIGH
3mm THICK

Q40 The drawings in Fig. 5:68 illustrate and give *outline* dimensions for a 12 V car inspection lamp.
(a) Draw a front elevation of the assembled body and lens.
(b) From this project a longitudinal centre-line cross-sectional end elevation. Include details of the bulb, a suitable reflector and the lens seating.

Q41 The photograph shows a battery powered lamp which is fitted with two switches so that it can show a white front light, or a red top light or both together. Figure 5:69 gives the basic sizes of a cycle lamp derived from it.
   Draw the following views:
(a) An elevation looking from A.
(b) A centre-line cross-section looking from B.
(c) A plan view.
Design and add a suitable mounting clip to the back of the lamp.

Q42 Figure 5:70 shows scaled down views of a woodturning lathe outrigger. Draw the following views:
(a) A plan in the same position as in the diagram.
(b) An elevation sectioned on A–A and projected from the plan.

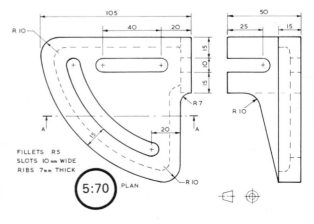

FILLETS R5
SLOTS 10 mm WIDE
RIBS 7mm THICK

5:70   PLAN

Q43 Figure 5:71 details the parts which make up the panel pin punch illustrated in the photograph. The rod end of E, together with the spring D, slide into C. This assembly then slides into B. Part B is a light press-fit into the body, A. The cap is similarly a light press-fit into the body.

With all the parts assembled in place, draw a longitudinal centre-line cross-sectional elevation twice full size.

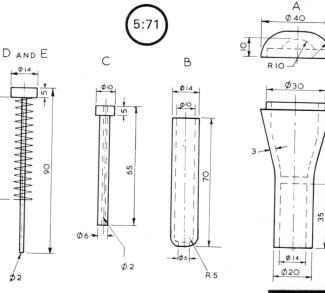

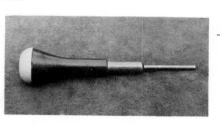

Q44 Figure 5:72 gives dimensioned details of the corking gun which is shown assembled in the photograph. The neoprene washer A, fits over the stem of the ram B, which in turn slides into the cap C. This assembly then fits into the body D.

Draw a front elevation of the assembled corking gun with the left-hand half of the drawing in outline and the right-hand half in section.

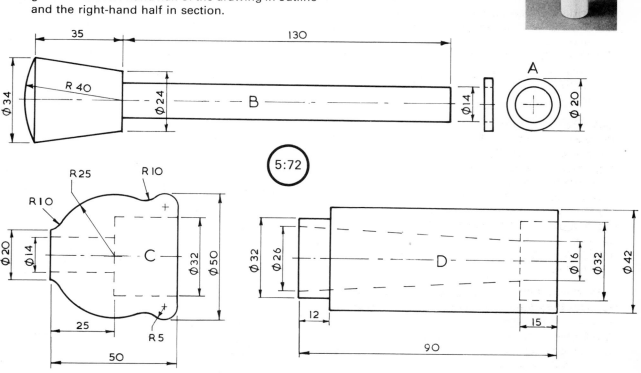

Q45 Figure 5:73 and the accompanying photograph give details of a co-axial television plug. The drawing shows the plug dismantled with its parts laid out in their correct order along a 30° line. This system of showing the order in which parts fit together is called an **exploded isometric view.**

Draw a longitudinal centre-line cross-section of the assembled plug four times full size. Omit part B. Show part A screwed 5 mm onto part D, as in the photograph.

The best method of drawing this kind of assembly is to start with the smallest internal item, in this case the 2 mm tube. Then build the remainder up around the tube by adding first part C, then D, and finally part A.

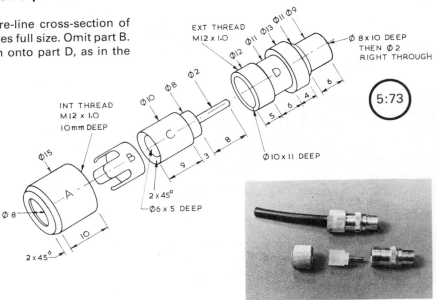

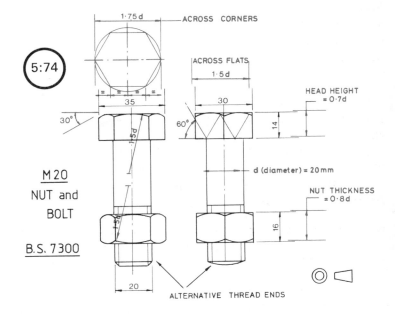

Drawing Hexagon-headed Bolts and Nuts

The dimensions shown in Fig. 5:74 are those specified as standard (British Standard 7300) for an M20 × 2.5 nut and bolt.

1 Draw the hexagon in the circle diameter 1.75d as a plan above the front view.
2 Draw the centre-lines and then draw the bolt head outline from the plan.
3 Draw the bolt diameter and position the nut thickness.
4 Draw the arcs using the methods shown.
5 Draw the 30° chamfer to the bolt head and nut in the front elevation only.
6 Draw the end view by the re-battment (45° line) method.
7 Add the thread end by one of the methods shown and include the thread depth.

AUXILIARY PROJECTIONS

A common problem in design draughting is the determination of the true shape of oblique faces. The solution to this problem can be found by projecting an auxiliary view at right angles to the oblique face (see Fig. 5:75).

The photograph shows a modern desk-top clock. Its body is formed from a circular section tube cut square to the axis at one end, and cut obliquely at the other.

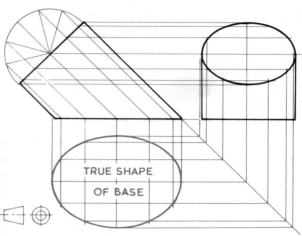

Any section cut through a sphere takes its true shape, a circle, when viewed perpendicularly. When viewed at an angle, however, the cut face always appears as an ellipse (see Fig. 5:76).

A sphere always appears circular, irrespective of the viewpoint.

When a cone is cut horizontally, as shown in Fig. 5:77, the perpendicular view of the cut face shows it to be a **circle**.

If the cone is cut obliquely through both sides the true shape of the cut face is an **ellipse**.

A section taken parallel to one side forms a **parabola**.

A **hyperbola** is produced by a cutting plane which makes a greater angle with the base than the side of the cone does. It is matched by an equal and opposite curve.

The outline curves of these sections (**conic sections**) can also be drawn by loci methods, i.e. they can be traced by a point that moves according to given conditions (see Book 1, Chapter 9).

A perpendicular projection from any face will produce its true shape.

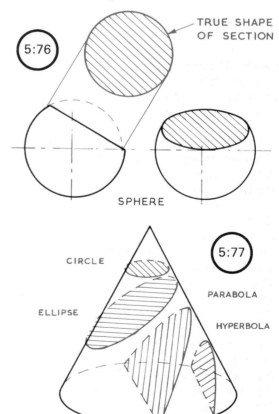

An auxiliary projection is an easy way of producing an oblique view of an object that will give a more interesting and informative drawing.

Figure 5:78 shows a sketch map of a church sited at a crossroads. The three drawings show the church when viewed from points A, B and C respectively. View C is the auxiliary view.

Figure 5:79 is a perspective sketch of an architect's model of a small bungalow which has one plain and one hipped gable.

Figure 5:80 contains an elevation, end elevation and plan view of the architect's model shown above. The drawing A is an auxiliary elevation projected at a viewing angle of 45° along the arrowed line B. The drawing C is an auxiliary plan projected along a 45° viewing line arrowed D.

Views projected in this manner from elevations are plans, and views projected from plans are elevations.

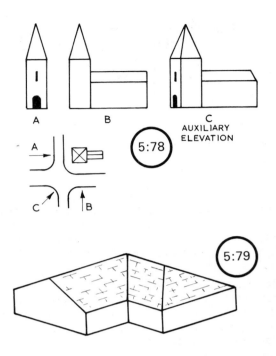

Q46 Copy the three orthographic views (Fig. 5:80) and add an auxiliary elevation looking from X (45°) and an auxiliary plan looking from Y (45°).

Auxiliary elevation lengths are projected from the plan and the heights transferred with dividers. Auxiliary plan lengths are similarly projected from the elevation and heights above the XY line transferred with dividers.

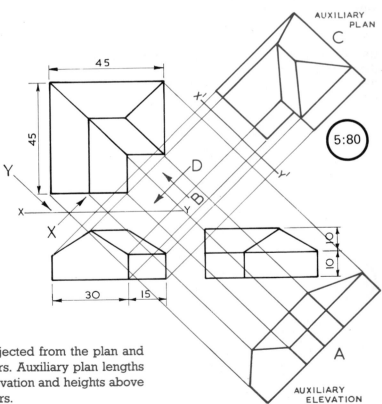

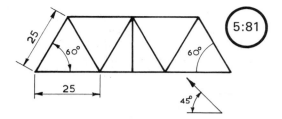

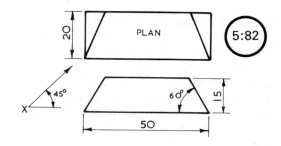

Q47 Figure 5:81 shows a lattice girder of the type used in Warren steel girder bridges. Copy the elevation full size and, by projection, show the framework when the bridge has swung open 45°.

Q48 The scale drawings in Fig. 5:82 show a roof to fit over a bay window. Copy the drawings and project an auxiliary elevation to show the appearance of the roof when viewed from a 45° angle as at X.

Q49 Figure 5:83 shows a scale drawing of a radio transmitter mast secured by three guy wires, each set at 120° from each other. Copy the drawings and, by projecting an auxiliary elevation, measure and state the true length of one of the guy wires.

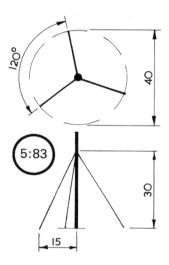

Q50 Scale drawings of a church with a square tower and a spire are given in Fig. 5:84. Copy the views to the sizes quoted and from them produce an auxiliary elevation viewed in the direction of arrow X.

Q51 Figure 5:85 shows the plan and elevation of the pattern of the facets it is proposed to cut on a gem stone. Draw the facets to the given sizes and project an auxiliary plan at an angle of 60°.

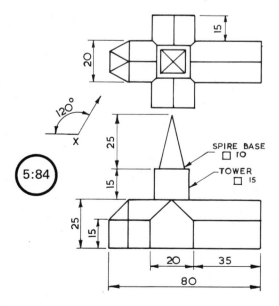

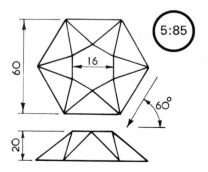

6 Electric Circuits

As with the individual parts of flow charts, the electrical components that make up a circuit are joined by a line—in this case representing an electric cable.

The circuits may take various forms and could be any of the following basic types:

wire circuit; printed circuit; silicon chip; microchip

The following examples are restricted to the wire circuit, which is the main concern, but the others should not be totally disregarded and could be investigated as additional areas for study.

WIRE CIRCUITS

The wire circuit shows the 'conventional flow' of electricity where it travels from a **positive** terminal to a **negative** terminal. The positive terminal is known as the **live** terminal. The negative one is called the **return**.

The switch is always placed first in line from the positive terminal of the battery.

In Figs 6:1–6:3. the components have been drawn pictorially. Since this is rather time consuming the **circuit diagram** method in Fig. 6:4 is used instead.

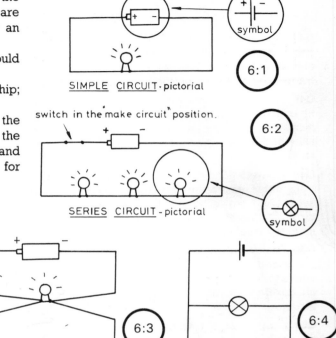

SIMPLE CIRCUIT - pictorial 6:1

switch in the 'make circuit' position. 6:2

SERIES CIRCUIT - pictorial

PARALLEL CIRCUIT – pictorial 6:3

CIRCUIT DIAGRAM 6:4

Q1 Draw the circuits shown above, but replace the components with the correct symbols and include a switch. The symbols are shown below.

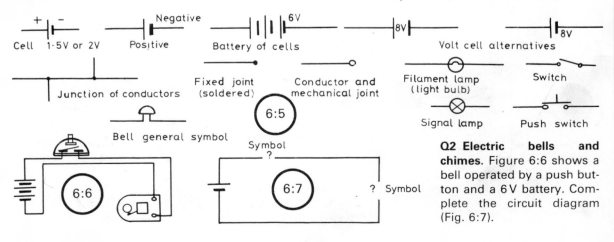

Cell 1·5V or 2V   Positive Negative   Battery of cells   6V   8V   Volt cell alternatives   8V

Junction of conductors   Fixed joint (soldered)   Conductor and mechanical joint   Filament lamp (light bulb)   Switch

6:5

Signal lamp   Push switch

Bell general symbol

Symbol ?

6:6   6:7   ? Symbol

Q2 Electric bells and chimes. Figure 6:6 shows a bell operated by a push button and a 6V battery. Complete the circuit diagram (Fig. 6:7).

SYMBOLS FOR ELECTRIC CIRCUITS

The graphic symbols shown below are in everyday use throughout the electrical industries and conform to the British Standards Institute recommendations contained in their publication BS 3939.

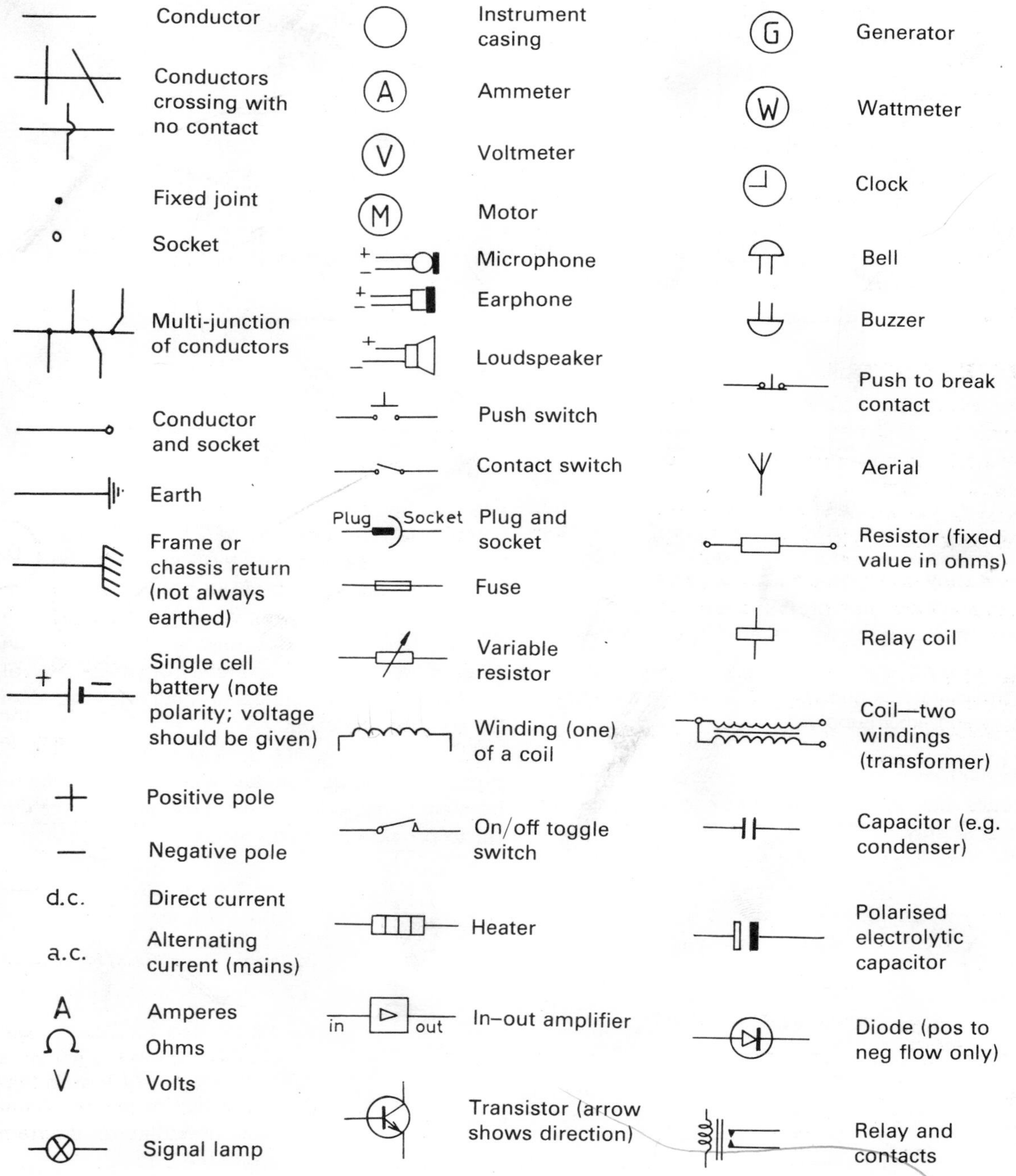

Symbol	Name
	Conductor
	Conductors crossing with no contact
	Fixed joint
	Socket
	Multi-junction of conductors
	Conductor and socket
	Earth
	Frame or chassis return (not always earthed)
	Single cell battery (note polarity; voltage should be given)
	Positive pole
	Negative pole
d.c.	Direct current
a.c.	Alternating current (mains)
A	Amperes
Ω	Ohms
V	Volts
	Signal lamp

Symbol	Name
	Instrument casing
(A)	Ammeter
(V)	Voltmeter
(M)	Motor
	Microphone
	Earphone
	Loudspeaker
	Push switch
	Contact switch
Plug Socket	Plug and socket
	Fuse
	Variable resistor
	Winding (one) of a coil
	On/off toggle switch
	Heater
in out	In–out amplifier
	Transistor (arrow shows direction)

Symbol	Name
(G)	Generator
(W)	Wattmeter
	Clock
	Bell
	Buzzer
	Push to break contact
	Aerial
	Resistor (fixed value in ohms)
	Relay coil
	Coil—two windings (transformer)
	Capacitor (e.g. condenser)
	Polarised electrolytic capacitor
	Diode (pos to neg flow only)
	Relay and contacts

GRAPHIC METHODS OF SHOWING ELECTRIC CIRCUITS

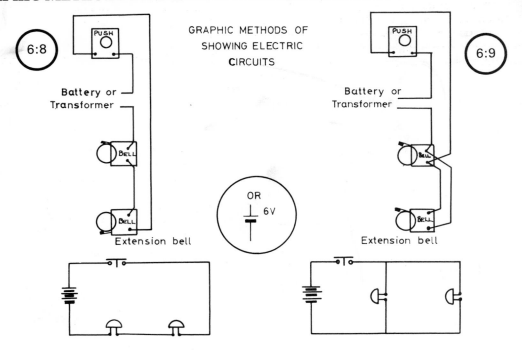

GRAPHIC METHODS OF SHOWING ELECTRIC CIRCUITS

Q3 The extension bell systems shown in Figs 6:8 and 6:9 are drawn in two different ways. One method is more useful to the do-it-yourself person and the other is better for the electrician checking circuits. Draw one of the systems as a circuit diagram. Name the type of electric circuit used.

Q4 Using the circuits in Figs 6:8 and 6:9, draw a circuit that has a push button, a warning light, two horns and a 6V supply.

It is important to note that, for electricity to flow, circuits must in some way return to the battery or mains supply.

Circuits in Cars

Circuits for car instruments and lights normally work from a 12 V battery system where the battery connections may be from positive to negative or from negative to positive. One terminal of the battery becomes the power supply while the other is connected to the metal body or chassis of the car. This connection is normally described as **the earth connection**.

All the instruments therefore have a power supply running to them and a connection is made from each instrument to the metal structure of the car to provide the earth return.

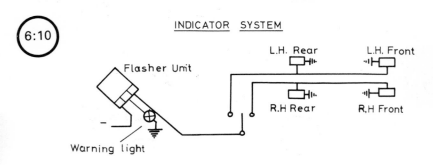

INDICATOR SYSTEM

The earth return may be to the positive or the negative side, depending on the design of the circuit.

Q5 Figure 6:11 shows a circuit containing a battery charger connected to a 240 V mains a.c. supply which is in the process of charging a 12 V battery.

Complete the circuit diagram so that all the components conform to BS 3939.

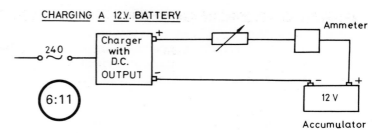

CHARGING A 12 V. BATTERY

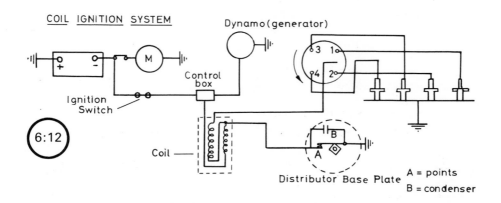

COIL IGNITION SYSTEM

Q6 Not all the symbols shown in the diagram of a car ignition system (Fig. 6:12) are recommended by BS 3939.

(a) Follow the circuit and find the 4 earth returns to the positive terminal.

(b) Draw the following circuits separately, using only BS 3939 symbols: (i) battery to starter motor; (ii) battery to dynamo; (iii) battery, through coil, to base plate (distributor) and to spark plugs.

Q7 Draw the circuit diagram which shows how to fit air horns to a car in place of the original horn. Use Fig. 6:13 to help you.

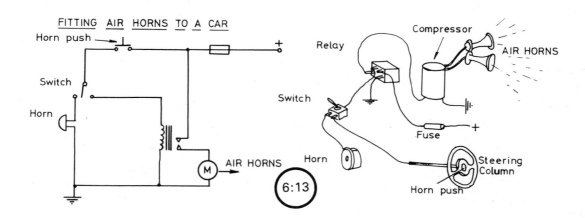

FITTING AIR HORNS TO A CAR

Processes with Electric Symbols

Both the diagrams in Fig. 6:14 show an acceptable method of drawing a machine component incorporating an electric circuit. The arrows indicate motion. Notes to accompany such diagrams should be clear and away from drawn lines.

Q8 An electric lawn mower has a power supply and a motor. The power may then be transmitted either direct to the propellor blades or by a belt via a shaft. Draw a diagram to show how the electricity supply drives the blades.

Burglar Alarms

Q9 Figure 6:15 shows the circuit diagram of an alarm system that operates a buzzer when a window is opened. The pictorial circuit explains the system. Devise your own system that incorporates two windows and uses a different method to sound the alarm.

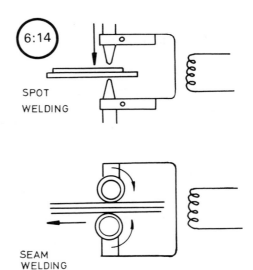

SPOT WELDING

SEAM WELDING

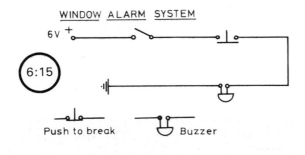

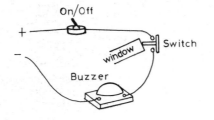

Circuits as Combination Locks

Figure 6:16 shows a circuit in which a lock is released only when the switches are in the correct positions. If the circuit is completed by pressing the push switch when the combination is wrongly set, the buzzer sounds.

1 Any number of multi-position switches can be used in series.
2 All the pins except the code numbers are wired together and taken to the alarm bell.

Q10 Design your own coded circuit using 3 or 4 multi-position switches. Do not disclose your code with arrows as in Fig. 6:10.

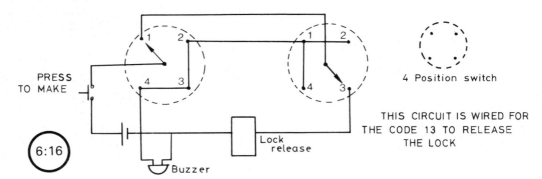

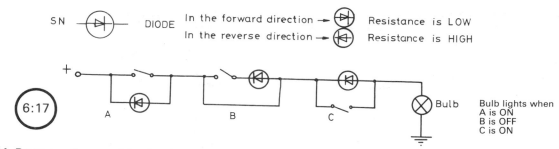

SN —⊕— DIODE   In the forward direction → Resistance is LOW
              In the reverse direction → Resistance is HIGH

6:17

Bulb lights when
A is ON
B is OFF
C is ON

Q11 Draw another combination lock similar to Fig. 6:17 to show how the electric current flows along the line of least resistance. Use a minimum of four gates and also state the switch sequence needed to the light the bulb.

Anodizing Aluminium

Aluminium may be coated with a metallic colouring by the electroplating process. The strength of the colour depends on the amount of time given to the anodizing process. The photograph shows industrial electroplating of aluminium.

Q12 Draw the circuit diagram and the pictorial circuit in Fig. 6:18, keeping both as clear as possible.

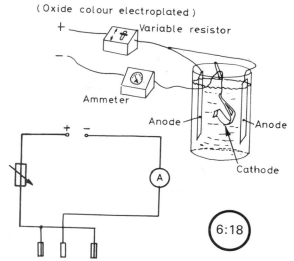

(Oxide colour electroplated)

Variable resistor

Ammeter

Anode   Anode

Cathode

6:18

7 Developments and Interpenetrations

DEVELOPMENT OF SURFACES

Many everyday objects, such as the outer shells of refrigerators, washing machines, cars and cookers, are made from sheet metal. Most of the food we buy comes packed in neat and colourful cartons which are convenient to handle. Most of these containers, whether they are made of metal, plastic or cardboard, start as flat sheets.

Over the past couple of decades a new industry has grown up—an industry that converts flat sheets of material into attractive containers, and which involves the designing and manufacturing of packages to carry consumer goods.

When designing such a container the draughtsman has to consider four essential points:

1 It must be cheap to make.
2 It should be strong enough to protect its contents from damage during transit and whilst being handled.
3 It should be convenient for packing and unpacking.
4 Above all, it should be attractive to prospective purchasers.

The photograph shows a box which has been designed both to transport and to display six wineglasses. Figure 7:1 shows the same box opened out flat. This flat piece of material is called the **development** of the box in the photograph. The diagram was produced by drawing each successive surface to its true size, and then joining the common edges of the surfaces.

This design provides double thickness on the ends and sides, as well as stiffened corners, all of which provide extra protection for the glassware.

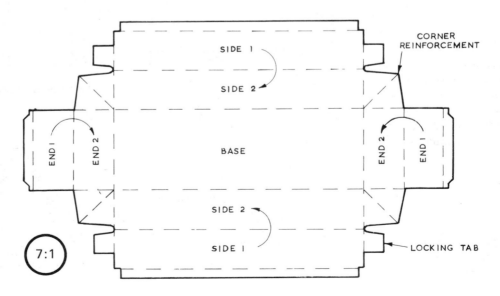

DRAWING DEVELOPMENTS OF THE FOUR BASIC SHAPES

Rectangular Box (Fig. 7:2)
Draw the base first and add successive sides and ends by laying over as shown.

Square Pyramid (Fig. 7:3)
Find the true length of the sloping edges and then draw each face in succession.

Cylinder (Fig. 7:4)
The development of the curved surface forms a rectangle the same height as the cylinder and of a length equal to its circumference.

Cone (Fig. 7:5)
The development of the curved surface is a sector of radius equal to the slant height of the cone, and of arc length equal to the circumference of the base.

All edges shown in a development drawing must be true lengths.

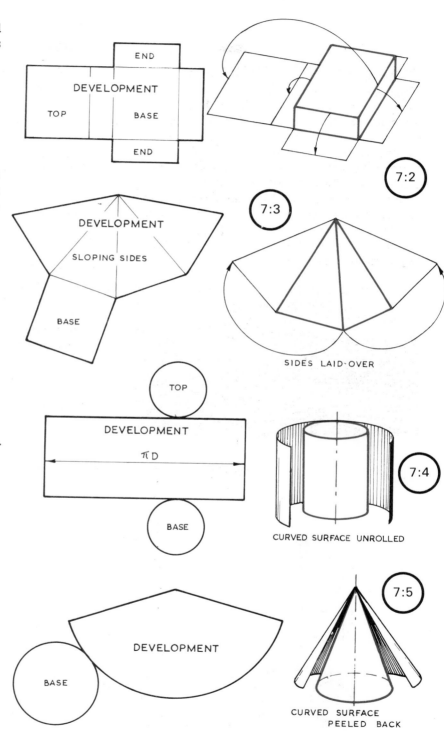

DEVELOPMENT
END
TOP
BASE
END

7:2

7:3

DEVELOPMENT
SLOPING SIDES
BASE

SIDES LAID-OVER

TOP
DEVELOPMENT
πD
BASE

7:4

CURVED SURFACE UNROLLED

7:5

DEVELOPMENT
BASE

CURVED SURFACE PEELED BACK

Drawing the Development of a Grain Storage Bin

This bin is made from a rectangular box which has been sliced through by an oblique cutting plane (Fig. 7:6). (This plane is an imaginary flat surface of negligible thickness.) A very great many everyday objects are derived from basic geometric solids which have been cut by such section planes.

1 Draw the base rectangle (50 × 45).
2 Add the back and front rectangles.
3 Using compasses, swing the length of the back and front edges through 90° (Fig. 7:7).
4 Join the four points as shown in Fig. 7:8 to obtain the true shape of the sides and complete the development.

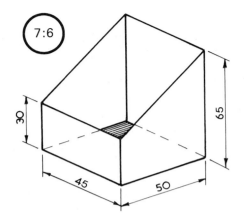

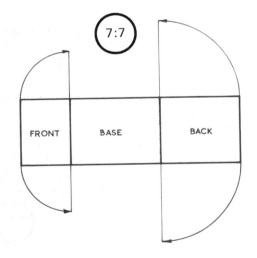

FRONT   BASE   BACK

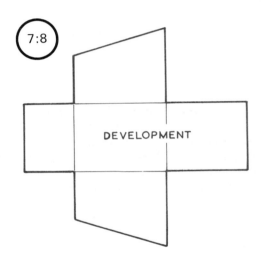

DEVELOPMENT

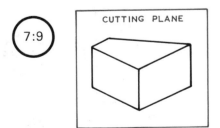

CUTTING PLANE

RECTANGULAR BOX SLICED
BY A CUTTING PLANE

Note the method of obtaining the true length of the sloping edge.

DEVELOPMENTS WITH SLOPING FACES

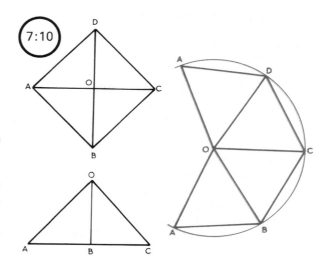

7:10

To Draw the Development of a Square Pyramid

The pyramid, shown in Fig.7:10, has a base 30 × 30 and is 25 high.

1 Copy the given elevation and plan.
2 Set the compasses to the true length of one edge (OA in the elevation).
3 Draw an arc centred on O.
4 Using dividers set to AB in the plan, set off the four base edges AB, BC, CD and DA along the arc.
5 Join all these points to each other and to the apex O to complete the development.

The line AOC in the plan is parallel with the vertical plane and therefore the edges AO and OC are shown in their true lengths in the elevation.

To Find the True Length of Oblique Lines

Figures 7:11 and 7:12 show two different methods of finding the true length of an oblique line.

1 Swing the edge OB (Fig. 7:11) through 45° to cut the horizontal OX in P.
2 Project P vertically to cut the plan base line extended in P'.
3 OP' is the true length of the edge.

The method of Fig. 7:12 consists of laying down a complete side of the elevation onto the base line and projecting its length onto the plan.

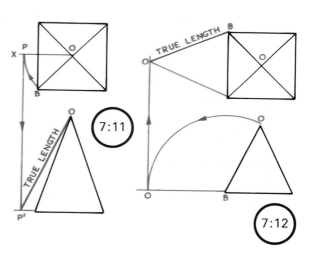

7:11

7:12

Q1 In the drawing of a hipped roof (Fig. 7:13) the true length of the hip rafters (the corner timbers) is not shown. Find the true length of the rafters.

1 Drop a perpendicular from O in the elevation.
2 Using O as centre and OA as radius, swing OA through to form the vertical OA^1.
3 Project A^1 to the end elevation.
4 Drop projectors from the end elevation to cut this line.
5 Join these two points to the apex, thus obtaining the true shape of the end face and the true length OA^2 of the hip rafter.

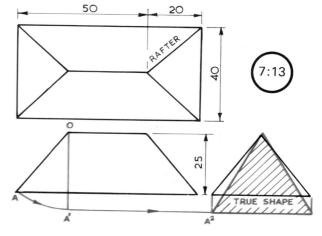

7:13

81

Q2 The photograph and sketch in Fig. 7:14 give details of a stainless steel egg cup. Make a full size development drawing if it.

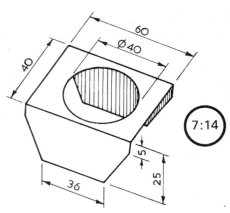

7:14

Q3 Make a full size development drawing of the stainless steel napkin ring shown in the photograph. Details are given in Fig. 7:15.

Q4 Figure 7:16 gives details of a folder of the type in common use in offices and schools. The two sectional views show the bottom and side gussets. Draw a development of the folder to one quarter size. Use your judgement for any missing dimensions.

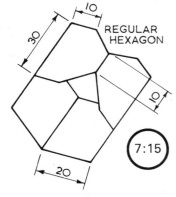

REGULAR HEXAGON

7:15

SECTION A A

SECTION B B

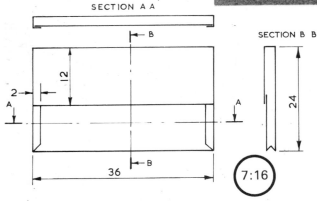

7:16

Q5 Figure 7:17 gives scaled down dimensions for a garden swing seat end frame. Using these dimensions, make a development drawing for a suitable cover. It should fit snugly over the top of the frame and follow the dash lines so that it may be tied down at each corner. The front edges are to be left open so that the front can be turned back over the top of the frame.

7:17

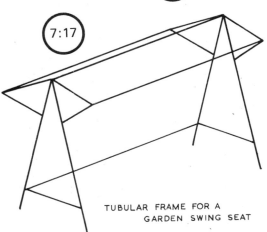

TUBULAR FRAME FOR A GARDEN SWING SEAT

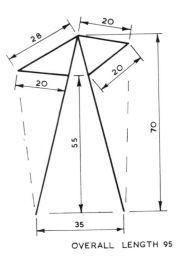

OVERALL LENGTH 95

Q6 Draw the development of the ceiling spot-light shown in Fig. 7:18. Omit the mounting plate.

Q7 Figure 7:19 shows a fume vent elbow from a dry cleaning plant. Draw a development of the elbow.

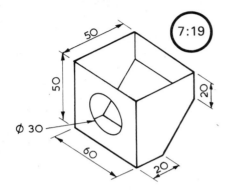

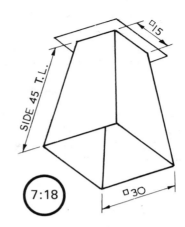

Q8 Draw the development of the cooker hood shown in Fig. 7:20. Assume that it is open at the back and the base.

Q9 Figure 7:21 gives details of a soldering/brazing bench ventilation hood. Make a development drawing of the hood, assuming that it is open both at the base and at the back where it joins the wall.

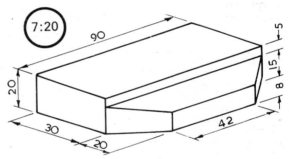

FORGE VENTILATION HOOD

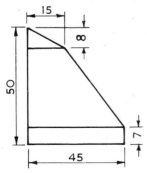

END ELEVATION VIEWED FROM A

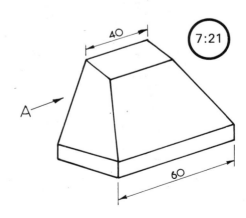

TUBE DEVELOPMENTS

To Develop the Curved Surface of a Cylinder

1 Draw the plan and elevation shown in Fig. 7:22.
2 Using a 60°/30° set square, divide the plan into twelve equal sectors. (This is the most convenient number.)
3 Project (unroll) the height of the development from the elevation. Using dividers, step off twelve spaces equal to the chordal distance across the arcs in the plan.
4 Draw in the vertical projector lines (generators). Number them as shown.

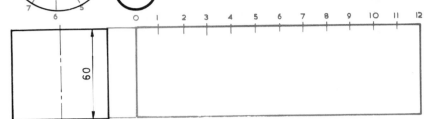

This method produces a development 1.1 per cent short but is acceptable in theory. Accuracy can be obtained by calculation using the circumference.

To Develop an Obliquely Cut Tube

There are many instances where cylinders are cut obliquely, e.g. for ventilators in sloping roofs.

1 Using Fig. 7:23, proceed as in points 1 to 4 above.
2 Starting with 0 as the shortest generator, insert the numbers 1 to 12.
3 Project the points where the generators cut the oblique face onto the correspondingly numbered generators on the development.
4 Join all these intersections with a smooth curve.

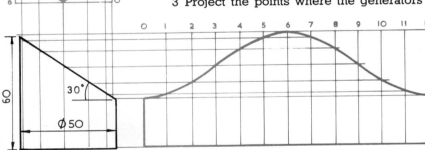

To Develop an Obliquely Cut Hexagonal Tube

1 Copy the plan and elevation in Fig. 7:24 and unroll the development.
2 Project the points in the elevation where the oblique face cuts the edges onto the correspondingly numbered edges in the development.
3 Join the intersections with straight lines. (Edges 1 to 5 are shown in this development.)

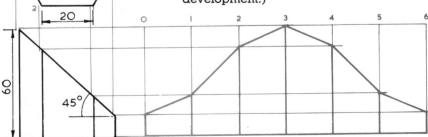

To Develop the Curved Surface of a Cone

The curved surface of the cone is unrolled in the same way as the cylinder, except that, as the apex is a fixed point and has no size, it remains stationary.

1 Copy the elevation and plan in Fig. 7:25.
2 Divide the plan into 12 equal sectors.
3 Draw an arc of radius equal to the slant height AB in the elevation.
4 Using dividers, step off twelve spaces around the arc, each equal to the chordal distance in the plan.
5 Join points OA and OB to complete the development.

To Develop the Frustrum of a Cone

1 Using Fig. 7:26, proceed as in points 1 to 4 above.
2 Project the division lines from the plan to the base of the elevation and from there back to the cone apex. Number them as shown.
3 Draw the generators in elevation and number them.
4 Transfer points where each generator cuts the oblique line in the elevation to the side of the cone to obtain true lengths.
5 Transfer these true lengths to the development. (Two methods, A and B, are shown. Method B is graphically clearer.)
6 Join all these points with a smooth curve.

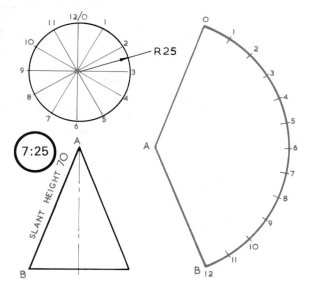

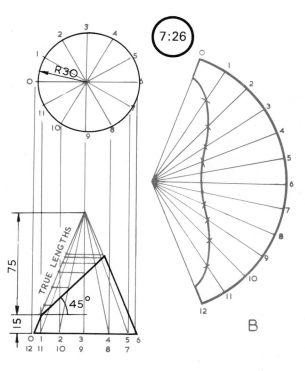

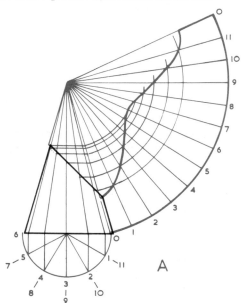

The sloping sides of a conic frustrum must be extended to intersect at the apex in order to find the slant height of the cone and thus the true radius of the development.

Q10 Figure 7:27 and the photograph give details of a cylindrical pen and pencil holder. Draw the development of the curved surface.

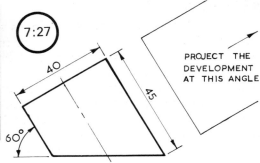

PROJECT THE DEVELOPMENT AT THIS ANGLE

7:27

40

45

60°

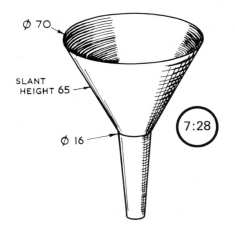

Ø 70

SLANT HEIGHT 65

Ø 16

7:28

Q11 Draw the development of the upper part of the funnel shown in Fig. 7:28.

Q12 Details of a liquid adhesive bottle are given in Fig. 7:29. Draw twice full size the following views:
(a) A copy of the given elevation.
(b) A plan view.
(c) A development of the label.

Q13 Figure 7:30 shows the development of a truncated cone which is part of a ventilator shaft cowling. Copy the development and from this produce a front elevation of the cowling. Measure and state angle X.

20

16

10

3

R5

25

40

7:29

22   10

R 6

CONICAL VENT

ROOF LINE

X

CEILING LINE

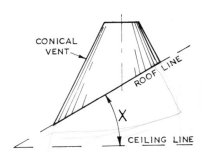

114   30

108

93

76

66

61

57

7:30

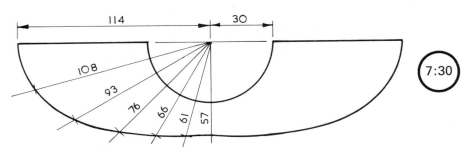

INTERSECTIONS

Modern air-conditioning in offices, factories and other large buildings uses a vast amount of ducting to carry the warmed (or cooled) air from room to room and from floor to floor. Before any of the ducting can be made, development drawings have to be produced. Joints must be made in the ducting where it changes direction, and it is of the utmost importance to determine the exact lines along which the various ducts intersect at these points.

To Draw the Intersection Lines and Developments of Two Square Ducts of Different Sizes Which Intersect at Right Angles (Fig. 7:31)

1 First draw the end elevation to determine A, the point of intersection.
2 Draw the front elevation and project A across to obtain A′ in the elevation.
3 Project the two heights AB and CD across to the development.
4 Obtain the length of the development by stepping off the perimeter of the large tube from the end elevation, using dividers.

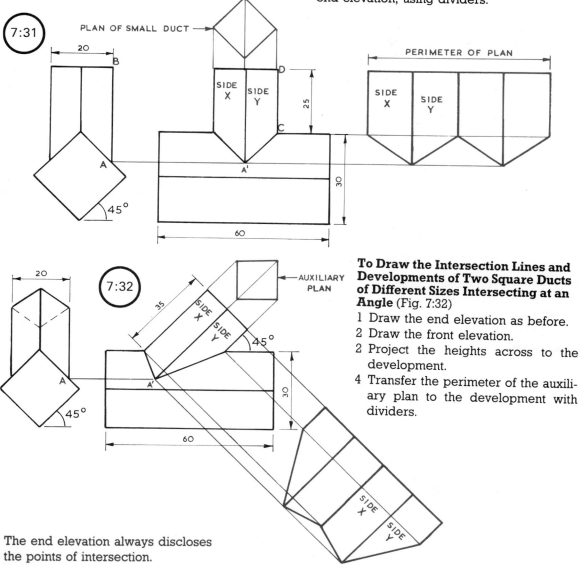

To Draw the Intersection Lines and Developments of Two Square Ducts of Different Sizes Intersecting at an Angle (Fig. 7:32)

1 Draw the end elevation as before.
2 Draw the front elevation.
2 Project the heights across to the development.
4 Transfer the perimeter of the auxiliary plan to the development with dividers.

The end elevation always discloses the points of intersection.

Cylindrical Pipes of Equal Diameter Intersecting at Right Angles (Fig. 7:33)

The development is unrolled in a manner similar to that shown in Fig. 7:22. To obtain the true shape of the hole, project the widths from the elevation and transfer lengths from the end elevation with dividers.

Cylindrical Pipes of Unequal Diameter Intersecting at an Angle (Fig. 7:35)

The developments and true shape of the hole are obtained by using the unrolling method as before.

Curves of intersection similar to those described here can be seen on the picture of a brazing torch head (Fig. 7:34).

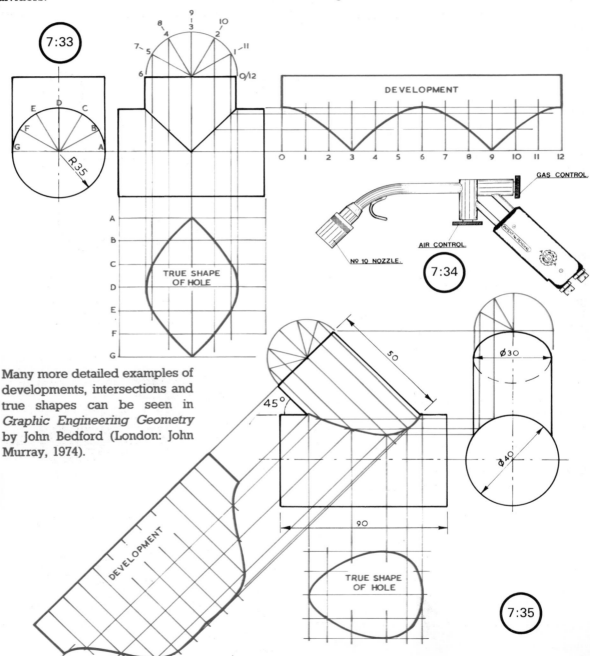

Many more detailed examples of developments, intersections and true shapes can be seen in *Graphic Engineering Geometry* by John Bedford (London: John Murray, 1974).

Q14 Figure 7:36 gives details of the profile of an aerosol cap similar to the one shown in the photograph. Draw the elevation, add the plan, and from these project an end elevation showing the curves of intersection.

Do not rub out the construction lines.

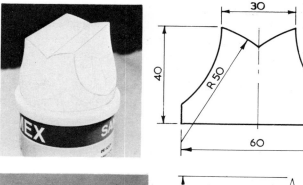

Q15 The photograph and drawing in Fig. 7:37 give details of a baby's feeding bottle warmer. Copy the elevation and add the necessary extra projections needed to provide a geometric construction for the curves of the intersections.

Do not rub out construction lines.

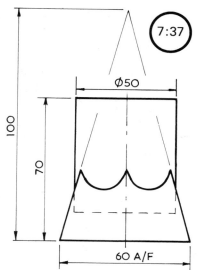

Q16 Figure 7:38 shows how to develop the curve of intersection at the junction of the handle and body of the plastic hairdryer shown in the photograph.

1 Draw the elevation and end elevation.
2 Divide the fillet curve, R20, in the elevation into a convenient number of slices.
3 Project these slice lines to cut the end elevation centre-line (e.g. A becomes A_1).
4 Project the point A_1 from the centre of the R15 circle to cut the R30 circle at A_2. Project A_2 back to the elevation.
5 Drop a projection line from the point where line A cuts the fillet to intersect at A_3. This is one point on the curve of intersection.
6 Repeat this procedure with the other slice lines to establish the path of the curve.

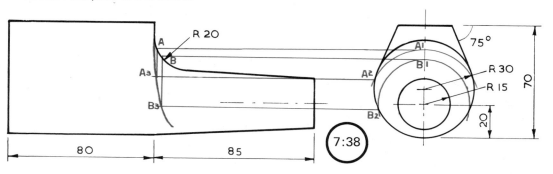

8 Loci

The locus of a point is the path traced out by that point when it is moving under stated conditions. For example, if a point moves so that it follows the shortest path between two points, its locus will be a straight line.

The study of loci is important for the design of machinery, especially the new robot-operated machines, since it can help the designer to find the most economical line of motion and provide sufficient room for moving parts.

The easiest method of finding the locus of any point in a mechanism is to construct skeleton drawings of the parts of the mechanism in a number of sequential positions, plotting the point in each of these then linking these points in a smooth curve (the locus).

Q1 A blackboard rule against the wall slips down as shown in Fig. 8:1. Plot the path traced by the centre handle as the rule slides down to floor level
1 Draw the rule and any convenient number of intermediate positions.
2 Plot the position of the handle in each.
3 Join these points in a smooth curve to form the locus.
In good drawing practice the points would be drawn smaller than in Fig. 8:1, and would not be seen in the finished drawing.

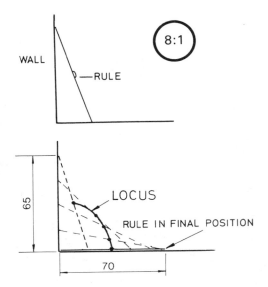

TRUNNION BLOCK AND SLIDER MECHANISM

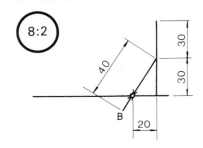

Q2 A window is fitted with a sliding rod and trunnion block so that it may be locked in any position between closed and fully open (see Fig. 8:2). Plot the path followed by the end of the sliding rod B as the window closes through 90°. Use a scale of 2:1. (A trunnion block swivels to accommodate the changing angle of the rod.)

Q3 The sugar tongs in Fig. 8:3 have three jaws that open by pushing on the plunger P. Copy the skeleton drawing and find out how far the end P moves when the jaws open through 30°.

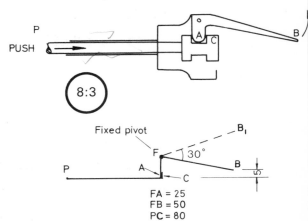

FA = 25
FB = 50
PC = 80

SPINDLE

SURFACE GAUGE

ROCKER ARM 'R' IS PIVOTED AT 'B'.

8:4

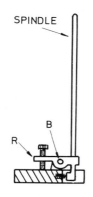

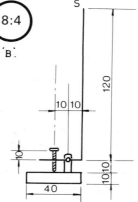

S

120

10 | 10

10 | 10

40

B

C

A

8:5

60

45°

C

B

15°

15°

P   A

A.B and C are PIVOTS

Q4 Figure 8:4 shows a surface gauge in which the knurled screw moves up and down and pivots the rocker arm R about the point B. Thus if the screw is withdrawn the vertical spindle S moves to the left. Find the furthest that the spindle tip can move. Give the answer in degrees of arc and in mm travelled.

Q5 The crane mechanism in the photograph is drawn at its lowest point in Fig. 8:5. In order to reach the *scaled height* of 60 mm, B has to lift through its maximum lift of 45°. C then rotates to the desired height.
(a) Copy the diagram, making AB = 65 mm, BC = 60 mm.
(b) Trace the path of C during all movements.
(c) State the angle at B when C has reached the required height, and give the distance PA.

Q6 If the sleeve is slid down the handle of the mop shown in the photograph, the sponge head folds and excess water is removed.
  Copy the diagram (Fig. 8:6) and plot the position of point S when the mop head has been closed to an included angle of 60°.

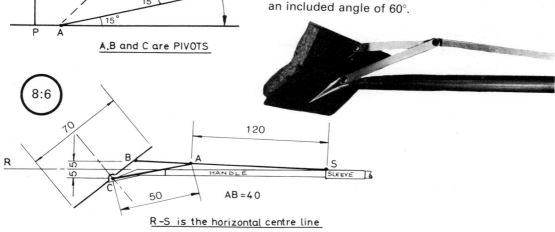

8:6

70

5.5
5.5

R

B   A   S

HANDLE   SLEEVE

120

50   AB = 40

R–S is the horizontal centre line

GEOMETRIC LOCI

Many loci form geometric figures in which the curved line follows a set mathematical formula. A select few of these curves are in constant use in both civil and mechanical engineering design. Some practical examples are given below.

Helix

The helix is probably the most common of all the special curves since it is the basic shape of all screw threads and coil springs.

To Draw a Helix (Fig. 8:7)

1 Draw the elevation and plan of the envelope of the helix.
2 Divide the plan into a convenient number of equal parts (usually 12).
3 Divide the height gained by one revolution of the helix into the same number of parts.
4 Number the divisions as in Fig. 8:7.
5 Draw projectors from the division ends in the plan to the similarly numbered slices in the elevation and so obtain points on the helix curve.
6 Join all the points to obtain a smooth curve.

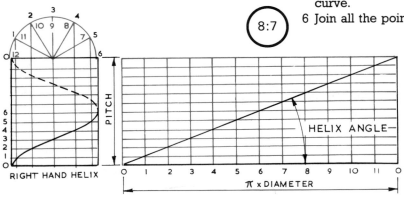
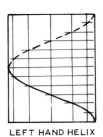

8:7

RIGHT HAND HELIX   π x DIAMETER   LEFT HAND HELIX

The locus moves around and along the cylinder in a constant and predetermined rotation.

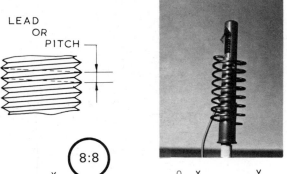

LEAD OR PITCH

The photograph on the left shows a popular game in which a swing ball is secured to a steel ring which is driven up and down a helix.

Q7 The propeller shown in the photograph below is 600 mm in diameter and pushes the boat forward 600 mm at each revolution.

Make a line drawing similar to Fig. 8:8 to show the path traced by the tips of the three blades during one revolution. Use a scale of 1:10 and choose a different colour for each blade tip. (Note: This is a left-handed propeller.)

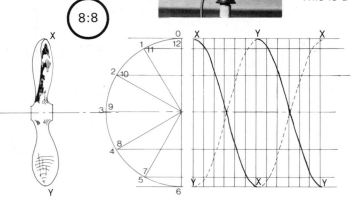

8:8

Ellipse, Parabola, Hyperbola

These three special curves all have certain properties in common: they all contain a **focus** inside and a **directrix** line outside the curve; the distance from any point on the curve is in **constant ratio** with the distance from that point to the directrix.

In the ellipse the perpendicular distance from the directrix to the curve is always **greater than** the distance from the focus to the curve.

In the parabola the two distances are always **equal**.

In the hyperbola the perpendicular distance from the directrix to the curve is always **less than** the distance from the focus to the curve.

Q8 Figure 8:9 shows the location of a navigation light on the River Thames. The deep water channel lies midway between the light A and the opposite shore (indicated by the median line S–S). Plot the course of the mid-channel deep.

Figure 8:10 shows that this course forms a parabola. The figure also includes a hyperbola drawn to a ratio of 2:1 and a part of an ellipse drawn to a ratio of 1:2. (If one of these two courses were followed the sailor could be stranded on a sandbank!)

The ratio set for any particular curve applies to all points within that curve.

Q9 Draw the road bridge shown in Fig. 8:11. The curve ratio is 1:1 and the scaled distance from the highest point on the curve to both the directrix and the focus is 20 mm (a scale of 1:200). The distance from the road level to the handrail is 1 m; from the road level to the bottom of the underpass measures 14 m.

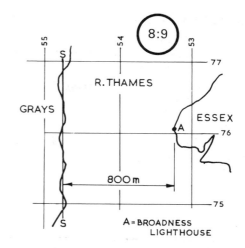

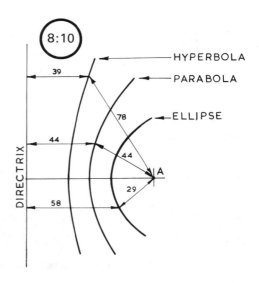

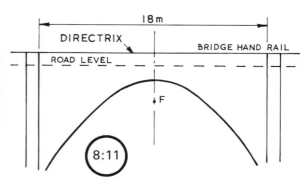

SPIRALS

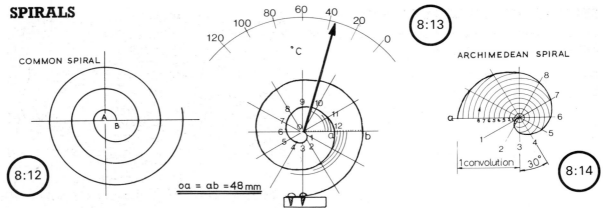

COMMON SPIRAL

8:12

8:13

ARCHIMEDEAN SPIRAL

8:14

oa = ab = 48 mm

Common Spiral

To draw a common spiral of 10 mm pitch (Fig. 8:12)

1 Draw the centre-lines. Set the compass to half the stated pitch and draw the semi-circle about A.

2 Using B as centre, set the compass to blend with the first semi-circle. Draw a second semi-circle.

3 Continue this process, using A and B as centres alternately, until the spiral is the required size.

Great accuracy and care are needed to keep the junctions between the arcs smooth and continuous.

Archimedes Spiral

Figure 8:13 shows a bi-metallic thermometer. As the temperature rises the outer strip of metal expands faster than the inner strip, and so the needle swings up the scale to mark the temperature. The curve the spring forms is called an **Archimedes spiral**, and is the locus of a point which moves around and approaches a fixed point by equal amounts.

Q10 Draw two turns of an Archimedes spiral with a convolution of 48 mm (Fig. 8:14).

1 Draw the straight line Oa and divide it into 12 equal parts.

2 Draw radials from O to form 12 equal spaces and number them as shown.

3 Using O as the centre and with radii O1, O2, O3, etc., draw arcs cutting successive radials 1, 2, 3, etc, thus marking points on the curve.

4 Join all the points in a fair curve.

5 Repeat the process for the second convolution.

INVOLUTES

The involute of a circle (Fig. 8:15) is the spiral traced by a point on a cord as it unwinds from a cylinder. Modern gear teeth are cut to this curve.

Q11 Draw the involute of a circle of 30 mm diameter.

1 Draw the circle and divide it into 12 equal parts. Number them as shown.

2 Draw tangents through the points on the circle.

3 Mark successive lengths along the tangents equal to 1/12, 2/12, 3/12 etc. of the circumference.

4 Join all the points you have obtained with a smooth curve.

Figure 8:16 shows the involute of a square. Successive corners of the square are used as centres and arcs are drawn from these to end at the extended sides.

Involutes can also be drawn on other regular geometric figures.

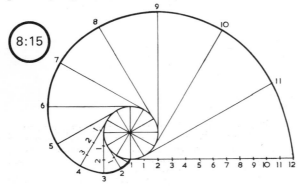

8:15

8:16

SPECIAL MECHANISM LINKAGES

The examples given below show how the study of loci can solve practical problems.

Pump and Piston Rods

The problem of how to convert the arc traversed by the end of the beam A into a vertical straight line suitable for pump and piston rods was solved by James Watt's parallel motion (Fig. 8:17). XY is the straight line portion of the locus.

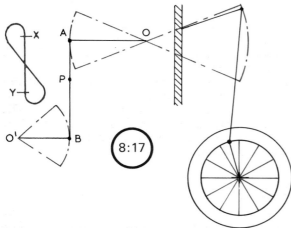

8:17

Q12 Draw the locus of the point P when OA = 60; O'B = 40; AP = 20; PB = 30.

Shaping Machines

Joseph Whitworth's quick return motion solved the problem of how to impart a slow powerful forward cut together with a swift load-free return to the ram of a shaping machine (Fig. 8:18).

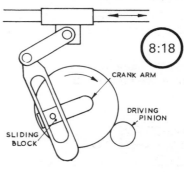

8:18

CRANK ARM

DRIVING PINION

SLIDING BLOCK

Q13 Copy Fig. 8:19 to full size.
(a) Determine and write down the maximum traverse of the ram, point D.
(b) Draw radial lines on the circle to show the limits of the forward and return strokes. Measure and state the magnitude of the two angles.

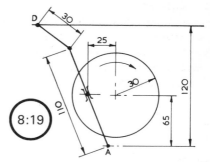

8:19

Q14 A coin rolls across a table without slipping. There is a small indentation or nick on the edge of the coin (Fig. 8:20). As the coin rolls through half a revolution, the nick rises to its maximum height. It then loses this height as it proceeds through the second half of the revolution.

    Plot the path of the indentation over one revolution when the diameter of the coin is 50 mm.

8:20

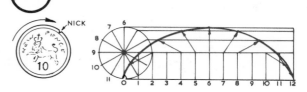

NICK

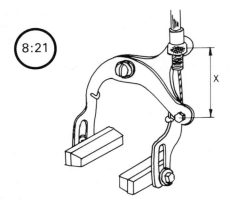

8:21

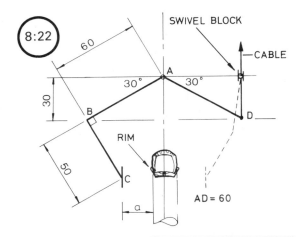

8:22

SWIVEL BLOCK

CABLE

30° 30°

A

60

30

B

50

C

RIM

D

AD = 60

a

Q15 When the brake lever is operated the distance X on the **bicycle caliper brake** in Fig. 8:21 is reduced. This closes the ends of the caliper arms and squeezes the wheel rim between the brake pads.

Assuming that the wheel rim is 20 mm wide and is set equally about the centre-line:

(a) Copy the drawing (Fig. 8:22) and measure and state distance a.

(b) Trace the path of point C when the brake is fully applied.

Q16 When the handle of the **mastic gun** in the photograph is squeezed the disc is pushed into the tube and sealant is forced out through the nozzle. Figure 8:23 shows the roller contact against the feed plate ready to push the rod and disc forward. After the handle has been operated the spring returns the linkage to the position shown. P is a fixed pivot. The locking plate prevents undue reverse movement.

Copy the solid lines and trace the movement of the disc for one operation of the handle.

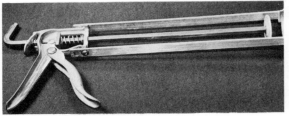

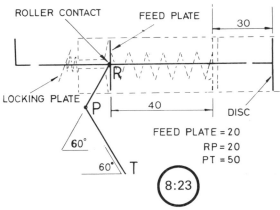

ROLLER CONTACT   FEED PLATE   30

LOCKING PLATE

R

P   40   DISC

60°

60°   T

FEED PLATE = 20
RP = 20
PT = 50

8:23

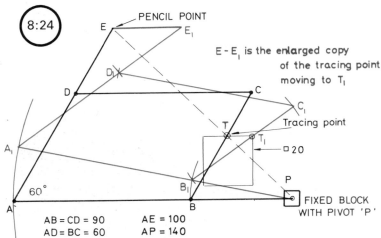

PENCIL POINT

8:24

E   E₁

D   C

D   C

A₁

T   T₁

□ 20

Tracing point

C₁

P

60°

B₁

B

FIXED BLOCK
WITH PIVOT 'P'

AB = CD = 90   AE = 100
AD = BC = 60   AP = 140

E–E₁ is the enlarged copy
of the tracing point
moving to T₁

Q17 Figure 8:24 shows a panto-graph in which points A, B, C, D and P move freely about their pins. The green lines show the position of the linkage when the tracing point has been moved from T to T_1.

Copy the drawing showing the tracing point at the corner of a square. By plotting the linkage for the remaining corners, produce the large square about E–E_1. Measure and state its area.

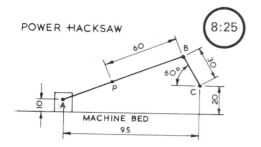

POWER HACKSAW

8:25

MACHINE BED
95

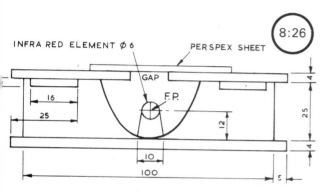

INFRA RED ELEMENT ⌀ 6   PERSPEX SHEET

8:26

GAP

F.P.

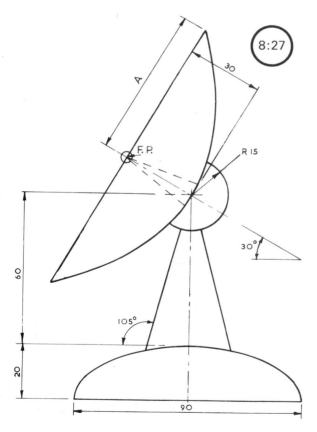

8:27

A

F.P.

R 15

30°

105°

90

Q18 The mechanism for a power hacksaw is given in Fig. 8:25. A, the crosshead, is driven forward and back by the link AB and pin B rotates around the fixed centre C.

(a) Determine and write down the maximum movement of point A.

(b) Trace the path of point P during one revolution of the crank CB.

(In this example the locus is an oval, not an ellipse.)

Q19 Figure 8:26 shows details of an infra-red heater used to prepare plastic sheet for bending. The gap is adjustable and the reflector is parabolic in shape (ratio 1 : 1). Draw to a scale of 2 : 1 the heating stand and the reflector.

Q20 A Small radar reflector is shown in Fig. 8:27 drawn to a reduced scale. The base is formed from half an ellipse and the ratio of the dish curve is 1 : 1. Copy the drawing full size and insert dimension A.

Q21 Figure 8:28 shows a mid-range elliptical speaker mounted within a metal frame whose ends are shaped as a hyperbola of ratio 2 : 1. Draw the speaker and frame twice full size.

It will be found helpful to draw the centre-lines first, then the hyperbola, and finally add the ellipse.

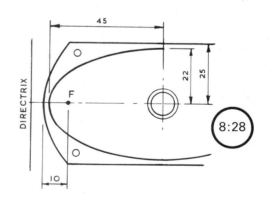

45

DIRECTRIX

F

22
25

8:28

10

97

9 Vectors

The movement of vehicles can be ordered by road signs; the paths of ships and aircraft can be seen from charts; and so straight lines can be used to show many different applications of movement.

VECTOR DIAGRAMS

A **vector quantity** is a line that has **magnitude** and a given **direction** in which movement is indicated. A **vector drawing** uses directed lines to represent a quantity (kilograms, newtons, metres, etc.) and the length drawn represents the vector's magnitude. The magnitude of a vector is **a scalar quantity**.

The line in Fig. 9:1 is scaled to show metres where 5 mm represents 1 m. As no direction of movement is given the line is a scalar quantity of 6 m and is *not* a vector.

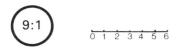

Figure 9:2 shows a similar drawing in which a direction is shown. This movement through 6 m from A to B is represented by the vector **AB**.

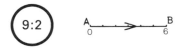

In Fig. 9:3 **B** is a vector representing a force of 10N acting at 30° to the horizontal in the direction shown.

Q1 A group of scouts travels from base camp a distance of 8 km in a SW direction. On the next day they travel 5 km in a NW direction. How far are they now from base camp, measured in a straight line?

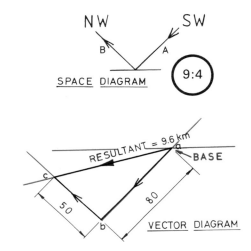

1 Draw the space diagram showing directions only, and not to scale.
2 Using a scale of 1:100 000 (i.e. 10 mm:1 km) draw ab (scaled length) parallel to and in the direction of **A** in the space diagram.
3 As the direction of the vectors must follow each other, **B** must be drawn parallel to the space diagram from the bottom of ab. Vector **B** will become the scaled length bc.
4 Enclose the two ends to form a triangle. The actual distance the scouts have moved from base camp can be measured from the line ca as a scaled length.

(a) Note that vector addition is *not* arithmetical—the actual length of vector **ac** is 9.6 km.
(b) Vector diagrams are completed by enclosing the vectors—in this case a triangle is formed.
(c) The direction of all the vectors in the diagram should be either clockwise or anticlockwise.
(d) The resultant is in the opposite sense (i.e. direction) to the given vectors.

98

Q2 A football is kicked 9 m infield from the corner at an angle of 45° to the goal line. It is then passed through 7 m parallel to the goal line and away from the corner post. How far is the ball from the corner?

Draw the two space diagrams in Fig. 9:5 and, by following the method in Fig. 9:4, produce the vector diagrams comparing your results. (Note the arrow directions.)

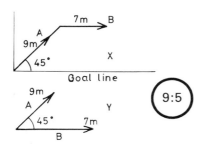

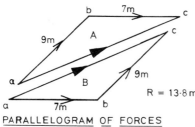

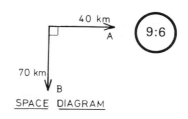

SPACE DIAGRAM

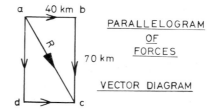

PARALLELOGRAM OF FORCES

VECTOR DIAGRAM

The resultant is common to both vector triangles abc and acb.

Q4 A ship sails 10 nautical miles Eastward and then 8 nautical miles due North. Determine its distance from its starting point and the direction (in degrees) it should have taken to travel the shortest distance. State the scale used.

This time *two* vector diagrams have been drawn, both satisfying the conditions in that the sense (direction) and magnitude of the vectors are correct. The resulting triangles are identical and if placed together would form the parallelogram of forces abcd.

Q3 Two trains start from the same station and travel at 90° to each other (see Fig. 9:6). Train A travels 40 km and train B travels 70 km before they reach their first stopping points. How far are the two stopping points from each other?

Use a scale of 1 mm to represent 1 km. Follow only the arrow directions to achieve one of the two possible vector diagrams. Use a shaded arrow to indicate the resultant.

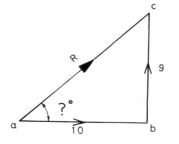

99

DRAWING VECTORS WITH SET SQUARES

Q5 A radar screen (Fig. 9:8) shows three lifeboats converging on a ship in distress. A is 45° West of North, B is 15° East of North and C is 30° East of South. Using set squares only and starting with centre-lines to show North, South, East and West (within a 100 mm square), graphically represent the ship and the direction from which the rescue craft are approaching.

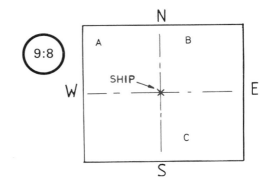

Q6 Figure 9:9 shows a road sign where roads A, B, and C are directed towards the given centre and stop at the circle as shown.

Find the distances AB and BC when the roads are of the magnitudes given in the diagram and at the following angles from the entry point (measured in a clockwise direction):

A—105°;
B—165°;
C—225°.

Set squares must be used.

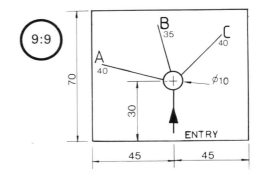

Q7 Figure 9:10 shows the boundary line of a cricket field with the bowler attacking from end B. His fielders were placed using end A as the starting point. Locate his fielders (1)–(10) when the circles are Ø100 and Ø40, and the wickets are 30 mm apart. Use set squares.

Fielders on the boundary:
 (1) Due East of A.
 (2) South West from A.
 (3) 15° East of North.
 (4) 30° East of South.
 (5) 15° North of West.
Fielders infield on circle Ø40:
 (6) Wicket keeper due North.
 (7) 30° South of East.
 (8) 30° North of East.
 (9) 15° West of South.
 (10) 30° South of West.

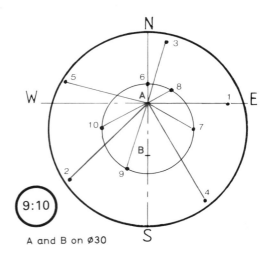

A and B on Ø30

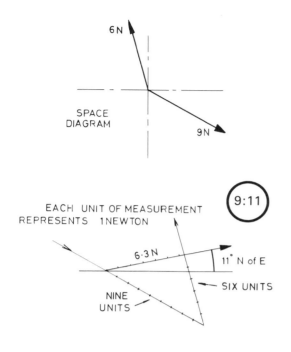

SPACE
DIAGRAM

EACH UNIT OF MEASUREMENT
REPRESENTS 1 NEWTON

6·3 N

11° N of E

SIX UNITS

NINE
UNITS

9:11

Q8 Find the resultant of a 6 newton force acting 15° West of North and a 9 newton force acting 30° South of East (Fig. 9:11).

POLYGON OF FORCES

Any polygon may be divided from one corner into a number of adjoining triangles, as shown. The method of using triangles to solve vector problems can therefore also be used when more than three forces are involved. In this case a polygon of forces is produced.

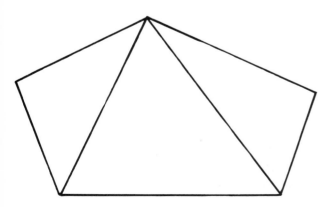

Q9 Find the resultant of the three forces shown in Fig. 9:12.

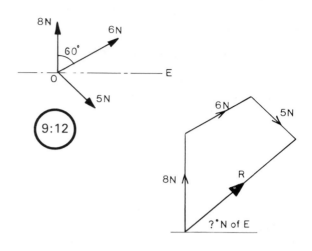

9:12

In the space diagram the vectors are shown originating from O, and all the vectors act outwards. Using the horizontal line OE as the starting point, draw the sides of the polygon parallel to the space diagram using a scale of 5 mm to represent 1 newton.

Q10 Find the resultant of the 11 N, 7.5 N and 5 N forces shown in Fig. 9:13.

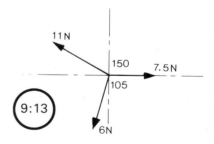

9:13

Q11 Find the resultant of the three forces shown in Fig. 9:14.

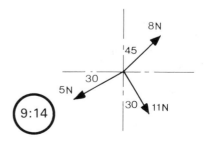

9:14

VECTORS OF FORCES

Q12 A 30 kN force acts at right angles to a 70 kN force. What single force can hold the two forces stationary?

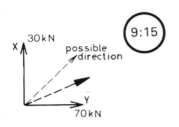

1. DIRECTION
2. MAGNITUDE
3. SENSE

Imagine two pupils X and Y pulling on ropes attached to a weight. The two pupils are at right angles to each other and have different pulling strengths. The direction in which the weight is likely to move is shown in Fig. 9:15.

The **resultant R** will be found by drawing the vectors in direction and magnitude so that the force **R** could replace the other forces without changing the conditions shown in Fig. 9:15.

The resultant **R** has sense opposite to vectors **X** and **Y**.

An **equilibriant force** which could balance the resultant must have the same magnitude as the resultant but must act in the opposite sense. Therefore, when the value of the resultant has been found the value of the equilibriant is also known.

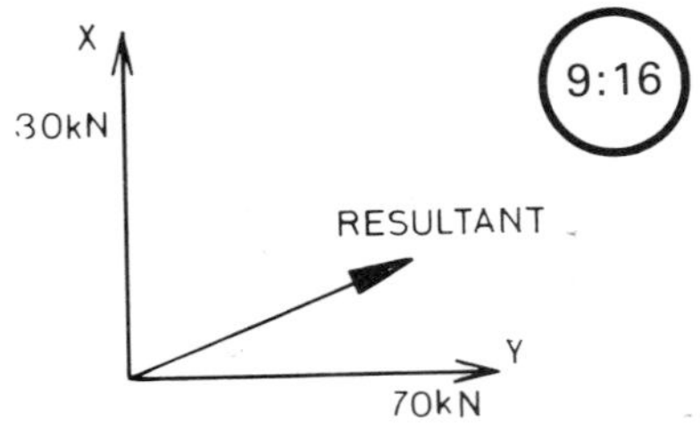

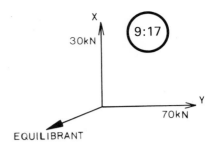

EQUILIBRANT

Figures 9:16 and 9:17 show the resultant and equilibriant in space diagrams. Notice that only the sense of the force has changed.

The equilibriant force can therefore hold the 30 kN force and the 70 kN force stationary.

Q13 Find the magnitude of the forces X and Y in Fig. 9:18 that will hold the force of 5 kg in equilibrium.
1 Draw the space diagram.
2 Use a scale of 10 mm = 1 kg to draw the known force **ab**.
3 Draw vector **ac** parallel to the unknown force X and extend the line.
4 Draw vector **bc** parallel to the unknown force Y and extend the line.
5 The triangle of forces is completed where **ac** and **bc** cross.
6 Measure the scaled lengths of **ac** and **bc** to record the values of the forces X and Y.

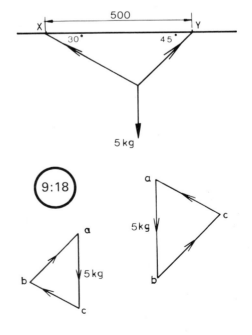

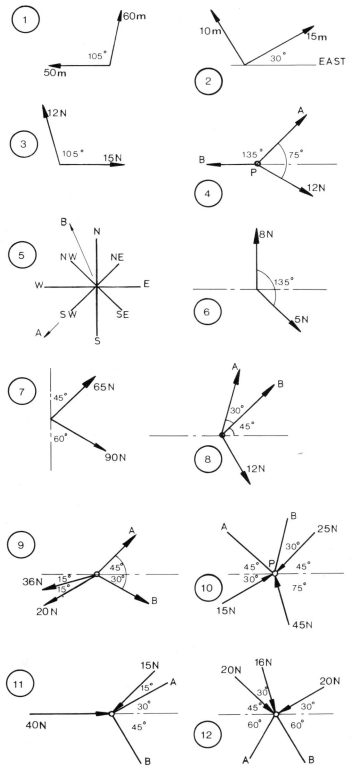

Q14 Complete the following exercises using the correspondingly numbered diagrams:

1 Two model aeroplanes are started from the same point. One lands 50 m due West, the other 60 m 15° E of North. Find their distance apart.

2 One wall of a house is 15 m long and 30° N of East. The other wall is at 90° to it and is 10 m long. Find the resulting diagonal measurement of the house.

3 A 12 newton force acts at an angle of 105° to a 15 newton force. Find the resultant of the two forces.

4 Find the values of the forces **A** and **B** that hold the 12 N force in equilibrium at P.

5 Ship A travels a distance of 30 nautical miles in a SW direction. Ship B travels NNW for a distance of 15 nautical miles. Find the distance the ships are from each other at these points.

6 Find the resultant of the two forces shown in the diagram.

7 Find the resultant of the 65 N and 90 N forces.

8 Find the magnitude of forces **A** and **B** which hold the 12 N force in equilibrium.

9 Forces **A** and **B** hold the 20 N and 36 N forces stationary. Find the values of the two forces by using the polygon of forces.

10 Use the pentagon of forces to find the magnitudes of **A** and **B** which hold the centre point stationary. State the sense of the forces.

11 Find the magnitude of the forces **A** and **B** which will hold the forces in equilibrium.

12 Use the pentagon of forces to find the magnitude of forces **A** and **B** which will hold the forces in equilibrium.

103

10 Charts and Graphs

ORGANISATION AND FINANCIAL CHARTS

These charts cover a huge range of activities, from running a little one-man shop to controlling the affairs of a giant, worldwide company. The efficient working of each demands the proper handling of information. The bigger the organisation, the larger and more complex is the volume of information to be handled. This has led to a widespread use of graphic communication methods which can reduce the masses of information and complicated figures to quickly and easily understood graphic displays.

The line graph in Fig. 10:1 shows the profit and loss made by a business over a period of ten years. An exact balance is shown by the line marked 0. Entries above this line indicate a profit and those below it a loss. At the end of each year's trading a dot is marked on the year line and when these are all joined together it can be seen at a glance that the company prospered until the very bad year of 1980.

The chart in Fig. 10:2 shows work days lost due to illness throughout various groups of skills. Taken from a recent survey, this shows that unskilled workers are most prone to illness and accidental injury.

The vertical bar chart in Fig. 10:3 shows the make-up of all the second year forms in a school. At a glance you can gain a reasonably accurate idea of the split between boys and girls throughout the whole year.

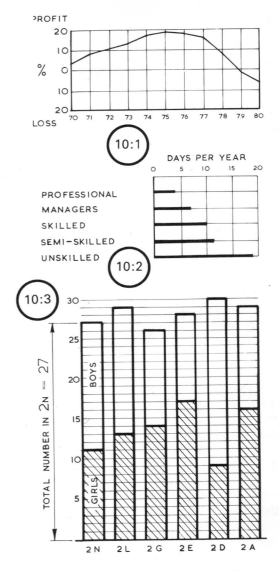

Line Graphs
Single line diagrams like Fig. 10:2 show the relationship between two variable quantities (e.g. m.p.h. and k.p.h., height and age, profit/loss and time). Each quantity is measured along *one* of a pair of axes that are usually drawn at right angles.

Bar Charts
These diagrams use columns to show a comparison of values. The columns may be displayed in a horizontal or vertical position.

Histograms
In a histogram the columns are vertical and normally touch each other so that the shape produced by the different values may be readily seen and interpreted. In order to achieve more flexible display methods, various column layouts have been developed—the main objective is to communicate the information as simply as possible and with maximum impact.

To draw either a bar chart or a histogram, rectangles are drawn to a scaled length within axes. Colour, shading, texturing and lettering are all used to provide the desired visual effect. Students should experiment with the various methods at their disposal, rather than concentrate on any one method.

Pie Charts

The circle is frequently used in Graphic Communication in the form of a pie chart. This type of chart looks like a round pie that has been cut into slices. It is also very easy to read and conveys its information at a glance.

Each of the slices in the pie chart represents, by its area, a percentage of the whole quantity. Since the area of a sector of a circle is proportional to the size of its angle at the centre of the circle, it is easy to divide the circle into the correct porportions by dividing the angle at the centre.

Figure 10:4 shows graphically the division of accommodation in this country. Almost half the houses are occupied by their owners, nearly one third are rented from councils and the remainder are rented from private individuals. Because the slices represent percentages, each 1% of the quantities is represented by $360°/100$, i.e. $3.6°$. So

49% owner occupancy is represented by $49 \times 3.6° = 176.4°$

31% council housing is represented by $31 \times 3.6° = 111.6°$

20% privately rented is represented by $20 \times 3.6° = 72°$

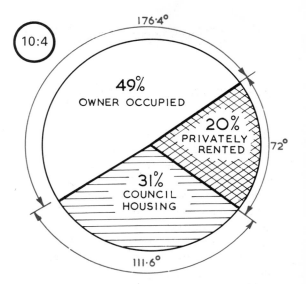

These degree measurements are normally not shown but they have been included in Fig. 10:4 to show how the circle has been divided.

Figure 10:5 shows the kind of work done by the group of people who own the houses in which they live.

Figure 10:6 illustrates the percentage composition of the air. Nitrogen comprises the major part, 78%; 21% is oxygen and the remaining 1% is made up of carbon dioxide and other gases. The angles at the centre of the circle are:

nitrogen—280.8°; oxygen—75.6°; CO_2 etc.—3.6°

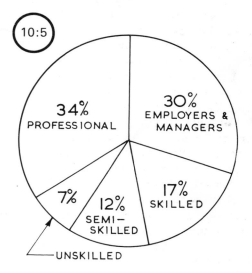

Q1 A house uses energy in various ways, from the central heating to a single electric light bulb. Display in a suitable manner how the energy for the whole house is consumed when the following figures apply: space heating 55%; water heating 20%; cooking 10%; appliances 10%; lights 5%.

Q2 The school tuck shop takes the following amounts of money for items sold during one term. Drinks £40; sandwiches £26; chocolate £15; gum and candy £15; crisps £48.

Display this information in a graphic manner and provide symbols to indicate the item each slice represents.

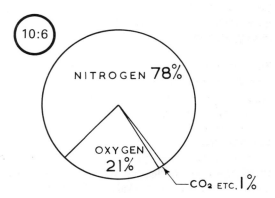

TECHNIQUES FOR CHARTS

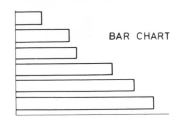

BAR CHART

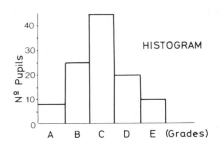

This **histogram** shows the range of exam grades gained by one year of a school.

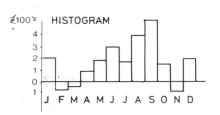

Birthrate for Dover

∅ Male
□ Female

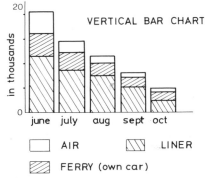

VERTICAL BAR CHART

□ AIR   ∅ LINER
∅ FERRY (own car)

A **vertical bar chart** to compare the numbers of holiday-makers travelling abroad by air, ocean liner and car ferry.

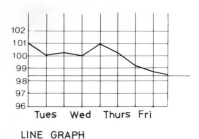

This **histogram** shows the profit and loss made by a school uniform shop over one year.

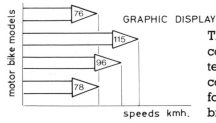

GRAPHIC DISPLAY

This **chart** uses a combination of graphic techniques to show the comparative speeds of four models of motor-bike.

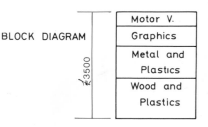

BLOCK DIAGRAM

The **block diagram** is used here to show how the Technical Department distributes its money to the subjects taught.

LINE GRAPH

The line graph here shows a patient's temperature over a four-day period.

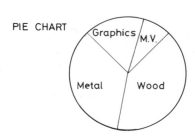

PIE CHART

The same information is displayed in a **pie chart**. In this case the total is not shown but the relative proportions are clearer.

The histograms in Fig. 10:7 have been used to show positive and negative values. The increase in positive and negative amounts may be indicated in colour by using darker or lighter shades.

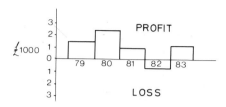

Q3 From the line diagram in Fig. 10:8 produce a histogram (with colour) that indicates the increase from intense cold to intense heat. You may add other examples or temperatures to the list. Use your own scale.

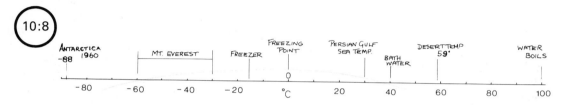

Q4 The histogram in Fig. 10:9 shows the stock of 35 mm film held by a photographic agency over the period of a year. The month of April shows the following figures:

Black and white	50 films
Colour slide	450 films
Colour print	500 films
TOTAL	1000 films

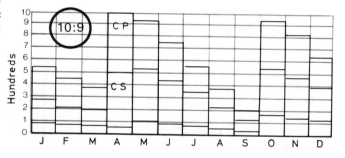

The height of each column gives the total stock of all film types in the agency.

Produce a histogram, using either colour or a texturing technique, that clearly separates the different types of stock held, yet still shows the total.

Estimate each figure from the diagram, but note that new stocks were bought in April and October. (Each column is 15 mm wide and 10 mm height is used to indicate 100 films.)

Q6 A car salesman sold a certain number of cars over a period of 7 years. Using the following figures, show graphically his progress during that time. Each axis must not be less than 100 mm in length.

Year	1976	1977	1978	1979	1980	1981	1982
Cars sold	100	90	150	85	40	30	65

Q5 Class Activity Find and state the months of the year in which the members of the class were born. This information may be written on the blackboard.

Individual Activity Produce a histogram that compares the numbers of boys and girls that were born in each month of the year (see Fig. 10:10). Use colour pencil or a pale tint in water colour to show the different columns for each month. State the scale used.

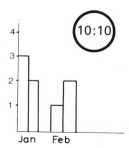

10:11

| Clear | Clear diagonals | Cross-hatched | Colour, Tone | Separate colour tones | Diagonal blocks | Multi-tone diagonals |

USING COLOUR

Figure 10:11 shows some methods of infilling columns on a chart or histogram so that separate sections can be clearly seen.

Q7 Pupils in Class 4X supported the following eight football teams:

A Fulham	E Liverpool
B West Ham	F Ipswich
C Everton	G Stoke
D Luton	H Tottenham

The results of each team's matches are shown graphically in Fig. 10:12. This attempt to show the differences in their performance has not clearly compared their results when there are 3 points awarded for a win, 1 for a draw and 0 for a loss.

Devise and draw a graphic method (*colour and shading should be used*) that would emphasise at first glance the league order in which the teams finished the season. Check this by stating the total number of points that each team gained. (W = win; D = draw; L = lost; each bar 10 mm wide; 4 mm vertically = 1 game played.)

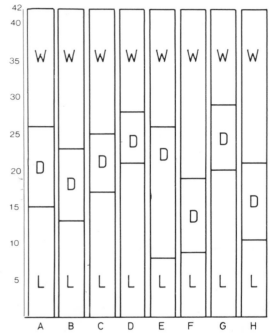

Q8 The horizontal histogram in Fig. 10:13 compares the adult male and adult female participation in leisure activities.

1 Redraw the chart to a suitable scale using colour to indicate the columns for males and females.

2 Insert pictograms, either inside or beside the columns, to replace the lettering.

3 Add a third column to indicate the approximate number of children involved in each of these activities.

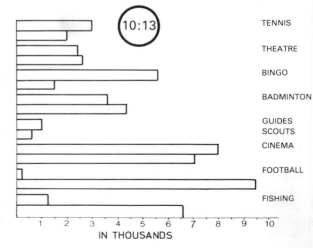

IN THOUSANDS

TENNIS
THEATRE
BINGO
BADMINTON
GUIDES SCOUTS
CINEMA
FOOTBALL
FISHING

108

Q9 Display the information in Fig. 10:14 using a technique that conveys the information quicker and more easily. The use of colour should be considered. The total size of the finished chart should be 280 mm wide by 140 mm high. Printing may be included *inside* each column.

A—High speed steel
B—High carbon steel
C—Medium carbon steel
D—Wrought iron
E—High tensile brass
F—60/90 brass
G—Copper

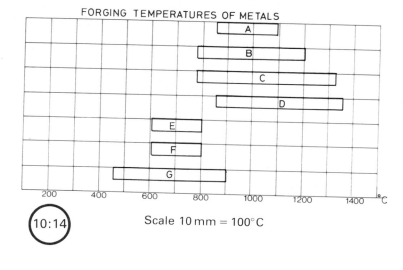

FORGING TEMPERATURES OF METALS

10:14

Scale 10 mm = 100°C

Q10 The price of seven car models (see Fig. 10:15) increases from 1 to 7. The performance of the individual cars also increases, as does engine size.

Produce your own bar chart (using figures from advertisements and magazines) that compares the cost of five cars with their top speed. Indicate the price of each car on the bar chart. (Each horizontal column is 8 mm high, there is a 2 mm gap between columns; 5 mm length represents 1 second.)

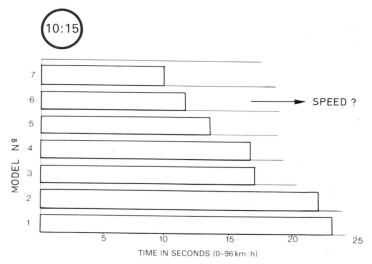

10:15

SPEED ?

MODEL Nº

TIME IN SECONDS (0–96 km/h)

10:16

km/h	Thinking distance	Braking distance	Total distance
32	10 M	10 M	20 M
47	15 M	22 M	37 M
64	20 M	40 M	60 M
80	24 M	61 M	85 M
96	30 M	89 M	119 M
112	34 M	120 M	154 M

Q11 The Highway Code gives speeds and their respective stopping distances in a table similar to Fig. 10:16. Draw a bar chart to show the six speeds and on each column indicate the thinking and braking distances needed. State the scale used.

ORGANISATION CHARTS

The chart in Fig. 10:17 shows a suggested sequence of operations that could be followed at meal times. With sufficient information it is possible to use this chart to design a kitchen layout that will be efficient—storage, seating and working areas arranged so that movement around the kitchen is kept to a minimum at this very busy time.

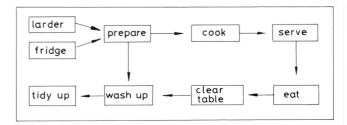

ORGANISATION CHART — Time and Motion study

10:17

Q12 Draw the kitchen outline given in Fig. 10:18 in a rectangle 140 mm by 60 mm. The depth of the breakfast bar should be 10 mm. Use the organisation chart in Fig. 10:17 to produce a well planned and organised kitchen layout. Graphic symbols should be used.

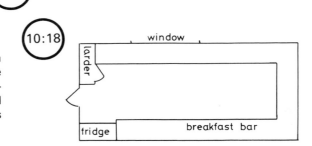

10:18

Q13 Answer part (a) *or* part (b).
(a) You are repairing a punctured inner tube that has been taken off the bicycle. Show, by means of an organisation chart, the processes you would follow to complete the repair.
(b) You are repairing a small tear in a pair of jeans. Show, by means of an organisation chart, the processes you would follow to complete the repair.

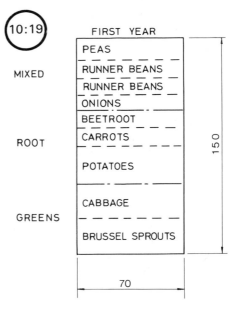

10:19

Q14 A plot of land is used for growing a variety of vegetables on a 3-year rotational system. The plot is scaled 1 : 50 and is shown by a rectangle 150 mm × 70 mm.

Design and draw an organisation chart that starts with Year 1 (shown in Fig. 10:19) and also includes the following two years of rotation. In each year the position of each crop must be shown. Colour should be used to separate the main crops of mixed, root and greens.

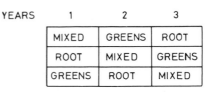

Route Finding

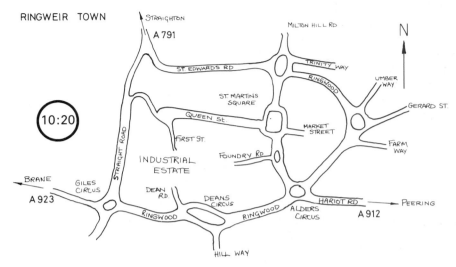

RINGWEIR TOWN

Q15 In Ringweir Town (Fig. 10:20) a paper boy has to deliver papers to the following streets from his employer's shop in Market Street.

Umberway, Farm Way, St Martin's Square, St Edward's Road, Queen Street, Dean Road, Foundry Road, Dean's Circus, Hariot Road.

Prepare a graphical organisation chart showing the quickest method of completing his deliveries.

Route Location

Figure 10:21 shows a much simplified method of route finding in which straight lines are used to link the towns. Major and minor roads have not been shown, but they could be included. They would have to be distinguishable from each other.

Q16 (a) Apply the method of Fig. 10:21 to produce a route location for Ringweir Town Centre (Fig. 10:20). The lengths of the roads need only be approximate. (b) Show by arrows a route that could be the quickest and easiest way from Hariot Road to the A791 to Straighton.

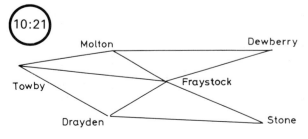

Q17 (a) Draw a freehand map of the area surrounding your home to distance of about 1 km. Name as many roads as you can and give the destinations of the main roads.
(b) Draw a straight line diagram of the same area. Omit the small bends, etc. but do not omit any of the information.
(c) Prepare a map for someone you are inviting to your home. Clearly identify your house and provide suitable landmarks. Read the notes below before you start.

Route Planning and Drawing

Details such as lakes, bridges, churches, stations, etc. are valuable landmarks. In all cases use a suitable symbol or colour system to identify these.

1 List the features you wish to include on your map and locate their position around your home using compass position and distance as guide-lines.
2 Include the major roads that should join most of these landmarks. Do not draw the roads too wide as this spoils the final appearance of the map.
3 Add the minor roads that link the major roads together and name or number these.
4 Carefully decide which landmarks are now to be used: too many will spoil your route map.
5 Finally, title your map to clearly establish the purpose of it and add any other information, in note form, that you feel is necessary.

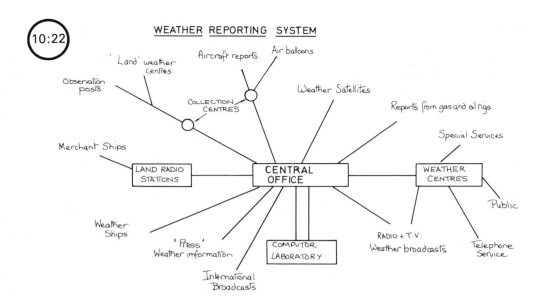

10:22

WEATHER REPORTING SYSTEM

Q18 The weather reporting chart in Fig. 10:22 needs to be increased in size and clarity to be a more valuable graphic communication. Reorganisation of the positions may help, as well as inserting pictograms to aid speed of visual understanding. Use A3 paper and colour where necessary.

There are many methods of communicating the organisation of large networks, such as that in Fig. 10:22, to the general public, including a variety of colour techniques.

You should seek out such examples by research, to broaden your graphic techniques and to enable you to produce charts with good visual impact.

Q19 Figure 10:23 shows a possible intercommunication system for a local police area. Information is fed from the national computer to the regional computer and then on to the local police stations for the mobile force. Reorganise it into the organisation chart which has been started on the right. Show how two-way communication is possible and how the chain is completed.

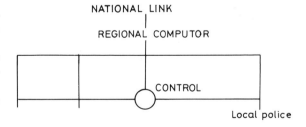

10:23

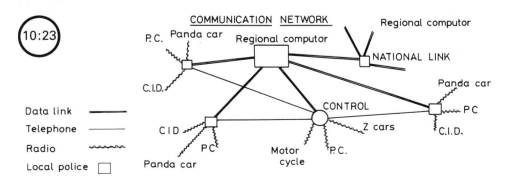

EXERCISES

Q20 An aircraft flying a steep turn has to tilt its wings to the horizontal to achieve an 'angle of bank'. When the angle of bank is 60° to the horizontal the following figures give the relationship between air speed and the radius of the curve needed to achieve the turn in a small aircraft.

Speed (knots)	50	60	70	80	90
Radius (metres)	37	53	72	95	122

Use a graphic display to show the relationship between the air speeds given and the relative radius of the arcs.

Q21 The following services may be found in grocer's shops: fresh bread, frozen products, cereals, wines and spirits, fresh imported goods, vegetables, newspapers, small packs of meat and bacon.

Choose two grocer's shops that you know and compare graphically the services that each provides by drawing a bar chart or a histogram.

Q22 The following electrical items are in common day-to-day use in most homes. Produce a visual display chart that clearly shows or names the items and also indicates the amount of electricity each uses in an hour. Consumers are charged for electricity in units of kWh (kilowatt hour—the amount of electricity used by 1000 watt equipment in 1 hour).

Iron, 100 W; hair dryer, 600 W; food mixer, 450 W; TV, 200 W; tumble drier, 2500 W; vacuum cleaner, 250 W; hi-fi, 100 W.

Q23 Figure 10:24 shows a rough draft of interconnecting services offered by a rail company to a large local chain of factories which deals mainly with exports but also sells directly to local customers. The rail company offers three methods of transport:

by road from the factory; by rail from container bases and terminals; by air or sea from container ports.

Draw a line chart using colour to show clearly the different methods and means of transport of all goods. The completed chart should be read from top to bottom and be clear and easy to understand.

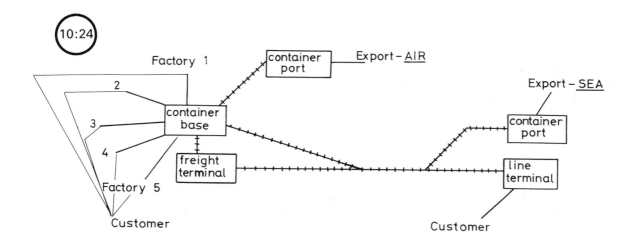

113

CO-ORDINATES AND LINE GRAPHS

A single 'point' or 'position' may only be located by relating it to other positions or lines that are already known. The line graph is based on this principle—here the axes are the known lines. There are many ways in which line graphs may be used; they may show statistics, relationships, comparisons or mathematical shapes as well as simply locating scaled positions of points on a designed item. In most cases a line graph is drawn from known lines which meet at right angles at a point called the 'origin'.

Example

A road traffic accident has occurred and the vehicles concerned have not yet been moved. The police in charge wish to note the positions of the vehicles for their reports. In doing this reference is made to road names as well as to the direction in which the vehicles were travelling, e.g. North.

A small diagram is also required by the insurance companies. Figure 10:25 shows the type of drawing needed.

No measurements need be given since these can be read from the graph. A was travelling North, it came to rest at $X = 2\,m$, $Y = 9.3\,m$; B was travelling South, it came to rest at $X = 3.2\,m$, $Y = 7.3\,m$.

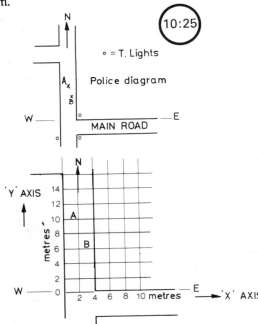

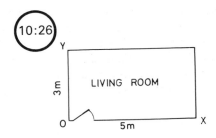

Q24 Use the X and Y axes to plot the positions of the following items in the living room shown in Fig. 10:26. Use a scale of 1:100.
(a) Table lamp: $X = 4.5$, $Y = 2.4$
(b) Footstool: $X = 3.5$, $Y = 2.0$
(c) TV: $X = 4.0$, $Y = 0.5$
(d) Radiator: $X = 0.2$, $Y = 1.5–2.5$

All distances are measured from the origin of the axes ($X = 0$, $Y = 0$).

Q25 The line graph in Fig. 10:27 shows a temperature chart of the sort most often seen in hospitals at the end of a patient's bed. A patient had his temperature taken at 8-hourly intervals over a period of four days, and the following temperatures were recorded.

Day 1	39.5	39.5	39.0
Day 2	38.6	38.3	38.3
Day 3	39.0	38.6	38.3
Day 4	37.7	37.2	37.2

Join the points to produce the patient's chart. (Normal temperature is 36.9 °C.)

Answer

The graph in this case should show only the eight-hour lines. On a hospital chart hourly divisions are provided since patients who are seriously ill need their temperature taken more frequently.

114

The line graph may be used to find information when a constant relationship exists between two quantities. For example, 8 km = 5 miles and 0 km = 0 miles. If this information is presented graphically as in Fig. 10:28, all other equivalents may be read from the graph.

Q26 (a) Draw the line graph in Fig. 10:28. Use 15 mm to represent both 10 mph and 10 km/h.
(b) Colour in the speed limit zones lightly.
(c) Find the speeds in km/h that represent 15 mph, 35 mph, 48 mph, and 64 mph.

Q27 The line graph which has been partially drawn in Fig. 10:29 shows known temperature equivalents in Fahrenheit and Celcius. Freezing point is 0°C and 32°F, boiling point is 100°C and 212°F. Draw the corresponding line graph using 1 mm to represent 1°.
    Graphically display the following temperatures:
        Central heating at 75 °F
        Tap water at 16 °C
        Bath water at 40 °C
        Film developing at 168 °F
        Body temperature at 98·4 °F
Colour is recommended to improve the visual effect.

CONTOUR GRAPHS

A contour graph is a line graph showing the height of land above and below sea level over a straight line distance. In graphs of this type the height is often measured in **metres** and horizontal distances are measured in **kilometres**.

As with all line graphs, the starting point or origin is at 0, but the scale on the Y-axis (vertical) is in metres and that on the X-axis (horizontal) is in kilometres (1 km = 1000 m). A slope gaining 75 m on the Y-axis and 2 km on the X-axis (point A in Fig. 10:30) is 27 times as steep on the graph as it is

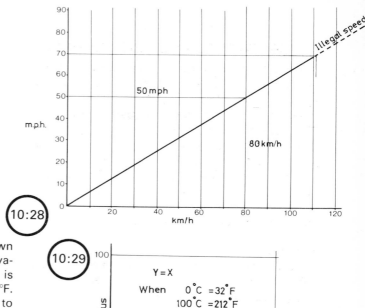

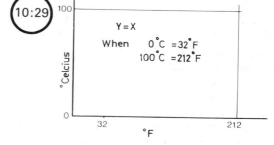

in reality; what is a gentle slope appears as a steep hill.

    To produce an accurate contour map, the scales on the X and Y-axes must be the same. Since this is impractical, the contour graph is used to show the general shape of the land and the distances from point to point, always remembering to make allowance for the lack of proportion on the X-axis.

    The information that Pole Moor is approximately 9 km from Huddersfield and is 225 m higher has been communicated graphically by Fig. 10:30.

Q28 Draw the map in Fig. 10:30. Use 10 mm to represent 150 m on the Y-axis and 10 mm to represent 2 km on the X-axis. State the heights and distances from Huddersfield of the named places on the map.

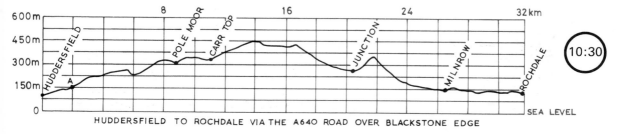

HUDDERSFIELD TO ROCHDALE VIA THE A640 ROAD OVER BLACKSTONE EDGE

115

Pedal Car Contour

Figure 10:31 shows a vertical outline of a pedal car. The scale could be increased without altering the proportions of the pedal car. In the figure the scales on both X- and Y-axes are the same and the measurements are thus in **direct proportion** to each other. This is known as being **in scale**. The scale has 10 mm on the graph representing 100 mm on the pedal car outline. The scale is therefore 1 : 10 or 1/10 full size.

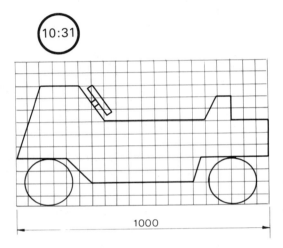

Q29 Draw the pedal car in Fig. 10:31 to a scale of 1 : 5.

Q30 The wheel base for a customised car is fixed by the distance from the engine to the rear differential. Design your own customised body shell, which must be in the proportion of 10 mm = 300 mm shown in Fig. 10:32. The position of the vertical axis may be changed if you wish to lengthen the bonnet or boot. Doors and windows must be shown.

Q31 Draw a contour map of a commonly seen object using a line graph to a suitable scale. You may select one of the following or use one of your own choice:

    boat, telephone, calculator (desk type), typewriter, lawn mower

Detail is not required; only the main shape should be drawn.

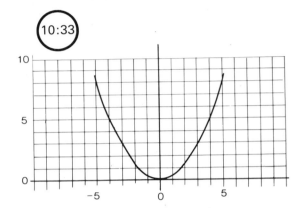

Graph Form $y = \frac{1}{3}x^2$

Although they look difficult, the graphs of this form are very easy to draw. Substitute values for x in the equation to find the corresponding value for y:

$x = 1$ $y = 1 \div 3 = 0.33$ point is (1, 0.33)
$x = 2$ $y = 4 \div 3 = 1.3$ point is (2, 1.3)
$x = 3$ $y = 9 \div 3 = 3$ point is (3, 3)
$x = 4$ $y = 16 \div 3 = 5.3$ point is (4, 5.3)
$x = 5$ $y = 25 \div 3 = 8.3$ point is (5, 8.3)

The points may be plotted and the parabolic shape of the graph found.

Q32 (a) Draw the graph of $y = \frac{1}{3}x$ (see Fig. 10:33) with 10 mm squares.
(b) Draw the graph of $y = 2x$ to the same scale.

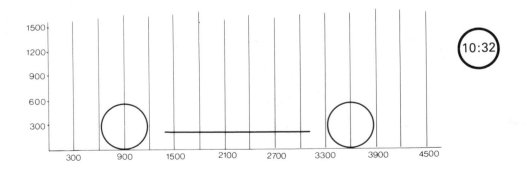

11 Design Problems

The following drawings show design problems that require a great deal of thought before a final solution is produced.

In order to obtain the best results the student is advised to follow the sequence listed below.

1 Read the whole question carefully.
2 Sketch possible solutions on scrap paper and check that everything asked for has been done.
3 Decide which solution best answers the question.
4 Check on the scale to be used *before* you start to draw.
5 Use light construction lines to map out the solution and check that your solution answers the question correctly.
6 Line and dimension your drawing.

Q1 A house has a small raised area at the rear that is to be covered by shaped concrete paving slabs that should not all be rectangular. Draw the scaled area as shown in Fig. 11:1 and, using slabs of various shapes, cover the area to produce an attractive finish. Colour should be used.

Q2 In Fig. 11:2 a living room is shown with a window in the psotion given. The owner wishes to fit units of furniture to hold the following items:
(a) individually placed carvings (a matched pair) on small shelves;
(b) a record player, records, cassette player, cassettes, and a small library (a single unit);
(c) two speakers (600 mm × 200 mm) 4 metres apart;
(d) a low unit (below window height) to hold drinks and glasses, with a display area under the top surface.

Design a layout to scale that fits the information given and is also pleasing in appearance.

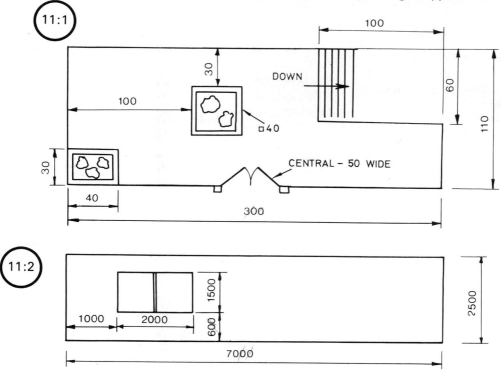

Q3 The four shapes outlined in Fig. 11:3 are of 6 mm thick material which may be wood, metal or plastic. Use these shapes or others of your own choosing that when put together would produce a modern and well constructed table lamp stand. State the way in which the pieces are held together and how the upright is fixed to the base.

Draw the completed design to a scale of 1:5 (including the shade in **front view**, indicating the materials used by graphic means. All dimensions of the lamp stand should be included.

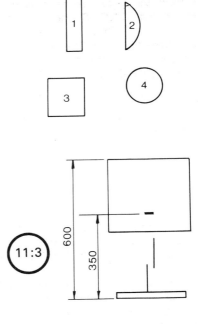

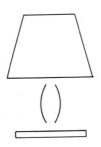

Q4 The photograph shows the top of a coffee table that has an inlaid design made from one large tile.

Design and draw in **plan** a tiled top suitable for one of the coffee table underframes shown in Fig. 11:4.

1 The shape of the top should blend with the base and should have a recess for tiles.
2 Some of the tiles should be patterned.
3 The tiles themselves should be laid out so that they make some sort of regular pattern.
4 All sizes should be stated, including those of the individual tiles and their number.
5 One patterned tile should be drawn to scale.

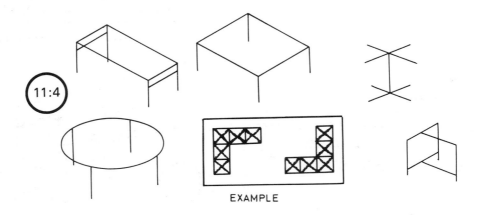

EXAMPLE

Q5 A speedometer from a car facia board is shown in Fig. 11:5. Speeds up to 180 km/h are given in 20 km/h divisions.

Draw the given figure and show on it by the use of colour or some other graphic technique the speed limits in the following locations:
(a) a town;
(b) a restricted zone;
(c) a motorway.

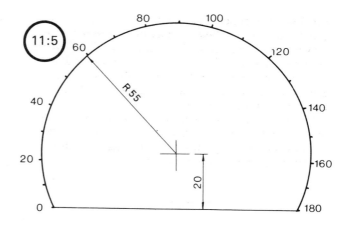

Q6 Figure 11:6 shows a magnifying glass of the type used by stamp collectors, engravers and the like. The stand is used to hold the glass when both hands must be in use.

Using freehand drawings only design a holding device at A and show how the magnifying glass is firmly held at B. You are required to supply *all dimensions*.

Q7 A section through a drawer handle is shown in Fig. 11:7. Draw a freehand sketch of the whole handle fitted to the front of the drawer in the diagram, but to a larger scale.

The drawer front is 350 mm wide and 100 mm high. The drawer sides are 250 mm deep and 80 mm high, with a thickness of 18 mm. The handle size (overall) is 150 mm × 40 mm × 30 mm.

Keep the two parts in the correct proportion when assembling.

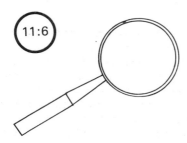

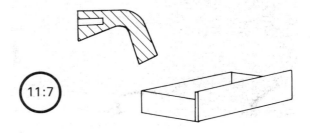

Q8 Use **four separate sketches** to show how the hasp and staple in Fig. 11:8 will each be fixed to the shed door or frame so that the two parts fit together exactly when the door is closed.

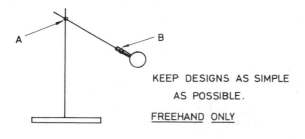

KEEP DESIGNS AS SIMPLE
AS POSSIBLE.
FREEHAND ONLY

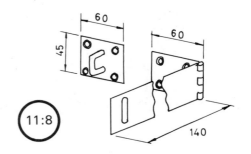

119

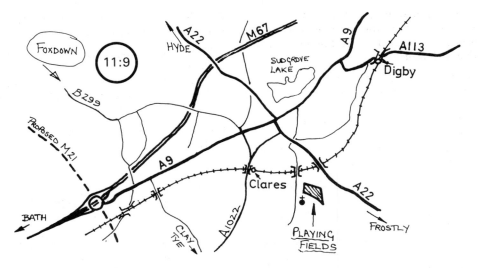

Q9 Figure 11:9 show a map of an area that contains motorways, main roads and minor B roads. The local scouts from **Foxdown** are meeting at the playing fields beside the church not far from **Clares Station**. The organisers need to supply a simple line map to help individuals to find the meeting point.

Design such a map that omits unnecessary detail but will ensure that everyone finds the playing fields.

Q10 The plan of a room which needs to be furnished is shown in Fig. 11:10. Draw the room to a scale of 1:20 and supply the following items of furniture in **plan**, to scale and suitably positioned.

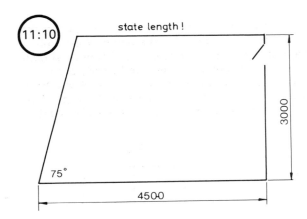

1 One settee 2000 mm × 700 mm.
2 Two armchairs 700 mm × 500 mm.
3 One TV 700 mm × 300 mm.
4 One low table 1500 mm × 500 mm.
5 One glass cabinet 1000 mm × 200 mm.
6 One pair of patio doors 2500 mm wide.

Rectangles only need be drawn.

Q11 Figure 11:11 shows an open stair leading from a living room up to the bedrooms. The stairwell has to be closed in for safety above the 400 mm wide 'string' that holds the treads and risers. There is already a handrail along the wall so the new fitting does not need to conceal totally the stairs and stairwell.

Your design should be modern and may be of any **suitable named** material. The structure should be fixed to the ceiling and to the top edge of the 400 mm wide string.

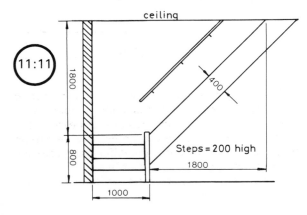

Q12 Lifebuoys similar to the one shown in Fig. 11:12 are to be sited at various places around a marina used by small craft. The following points have to be considered:

1 The buoy should slide easily off the stand.
2 A compartment to house the nylon rope line is required.
3 An area is needed on which instructions for use can be displayed.
4 The whole unit should have a pleasing shape.
5 The buoy must be seen easily.

(a) Design and draw solutions to the problem in sketch form.
(b) Draw the completed **front view** of the stand and give the main dimensions.
(c) Use colour so that the whole unit can be seen easily during the day and consider the possibility of night-time use.

Q13 Design a holder for up to 40 cassettes. It should conform to the following specifications:

1 The edges of the cassette boxes should be easy to see.
2 The whole unit should be stable at all times.
3 Access to the cassettes should be easy, as should their removal.

The dimensions of a cassette box are given in Fig. 11:13.

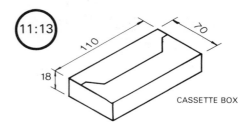

CASSETTE BOX

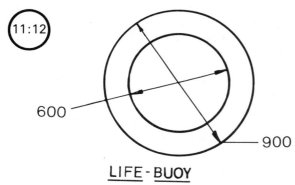

LIFE - BUOY

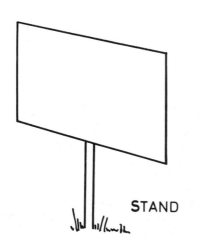

STAND

Q14 A football club wishes to display a pictogram on its own club holdalls. The name of the club is **Pegasus** (the winged horse). The pictogram should be bold and simple in shape and clearly seen.

Draw the holdall shown in Fig. 11:14 and from preliminary sketches produce a final design. Two colours only should be used. Use a scale of 1:5.

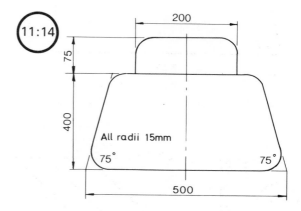

All radii 15mm

Q15 At a large exhibition a plumbing and heating engineering company wishes to show, above their display area, the various methods of heating that they can incorporate into a home. Design simple symbols that clearly show the differences between the following power sources of heat:

electricity, gas, oil, solid fuel, solar power, portable butane gas.

Q16 Two types of screen block are shown in the photographs above, in use as part of dividing garden walls.

Design a screen block that is pleasing in shape, is simple and contains arcs and straight lines within its square outline. Geometric constructions **only** may be used.

Q17 Figure 11:15 shows two blank dials of the type used in modern instrumentation.

(a) Complete dial A for use by a pilot to check the angle of the aircraft (shown by a symbol) to the artificial horizon (shown graphically) during flight.

(b) Complete dial B for use in a submarine to show the angle to the horizontal at which the submarine is travelling when submerged. **Symbols** must be used.

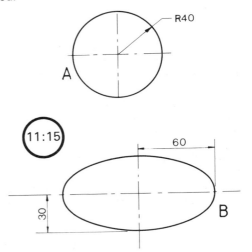

Q18 The photograph shows an ornamental well built in a garden from excess building materials. Design another well using different shapes for the main construction. The well should not be more than 2000 mm high and 1500 mm wide.

(a) Produce a scaled drawing suitable for a builder to complete the well without seeking further information.

(b) Add a freehand pictorial sketch that should include the use of colour or texturing.

The scale used should be stated.

12 Examination Questions

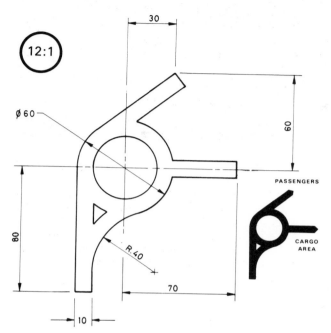

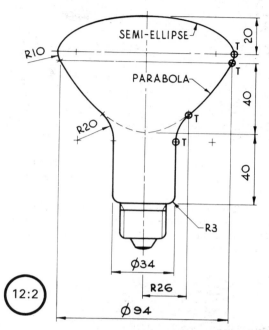

Q1 An airport traffic directional board is shown in Fig. 12:1, together with a suitably dimensioned diagram.

Copy the diagram, full size to the dimensions given, showing clearly all geometrical construction and points of tangency. (*EAEB*)

Q2 Figure 12:2 shows the profile of a reflector display bulb.

Draw, full size, the right-hand half of the glass part of the bulb. Show clearly the construction for the points of tangency indicated by $\oplus_T$ in the figure.

N.B. Begin by constructing the part parabola. (*SUJB*)

Q3 Figure 12:3 shows the cross-section of a silver bowl made in two pieces. The bowl cross-section is half elliptical, supported on a foot of base diameter 70 which meets the elliptical bowl tangentially.

To a scale of full size:
(a) Draw the elliptical portion, using a geometrical method and establish the points of tangency.
(b) Determine the centre of the R15 of the foot and from it complete the section. (*WJEC*)

Q4 The outline of part of a cover for a car wheel is shown in Fig. 12:4.

Using the given centres A and B make an accurate scale 1:1 drawing of the outline and the central hole. Do not include the bolt heads. (*WMEB*)

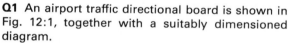

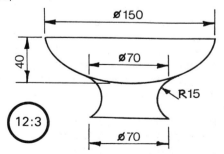

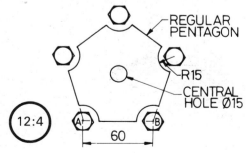

123

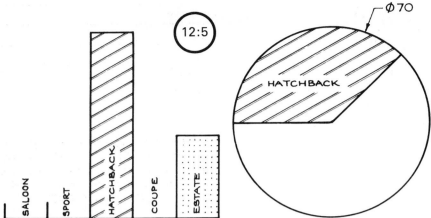

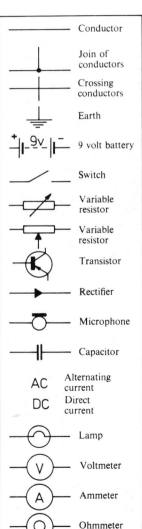

Q5 A garage recently sold 360 cars of which there were: 90 saloons, 30 Sports, 135 Hatchbacks, 45 Coupés and 60 Estates. Complete the two graphs in Fig. 12:5 to show the car sales.(*EMREB*)

Q6 Figure 12:6 shows components assembled together for a transistor testing device. When the switch is placed in the ON position, the variable resistors can be adjusted to obtain readings in order to test the efficiency of the transistor. With the aid of instruments and incorporating electrical symbols from those given on the right, draw an accurate electrical circuit for the device. (*LU*)

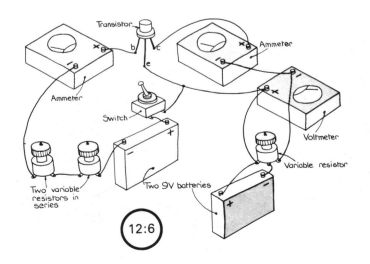

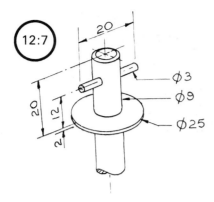

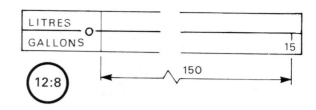

Q8 By geometric construction prepare a conversion scale, similar to Fig. 12:8, to compare litres with gallons. Graduate the scale in 5 litre and 1 gallon units to a maximum of 15 gallons.

1 litre = 0.22 gallon. (*SUJB*)

Q7 A wall mounted rack is required for use in a kitchen to store three beaters from a food mixer when they are not in use. The rack should be designed in such as way that the centre lines of the beaters are 90 mm apart and at least 60 mm from the wall.

Each beater weighs approximately 170 g (6 ounces).

Figure 12:7 gives details of the shank and drive pin of one of the beaters, and the beaters should be supported by these features.

Using your judgement for materials, sizes and details, draw in orthographic projection such views as are necessary to convey your design ideas for a suitable rack. Provided that you state the scale of your drawing, you need not add dimensions, but you should state the material or materials to be used in view of the use in a kitchen and of the possible production methods. (*WJEC*)

Q9 Part of an engineering component is shown in Fig. 12:9.

Draw, full size, in first angle orthographic projection, the following views.

(a) Front view from arrow F.

(b) End view from arrow E.

(c) Plan from arrow P.

Carefully plot the curve of interpenetration. (*NREB*)

Q10 Figure 12:10 shows an overflow pipe extending from a cistern into a washbasin. It is decided to cover it with wallpaper.

Construct, scale 1:1, a development (net) of the required paper with the seam centrally under the pipe. (*O & CSEB*)

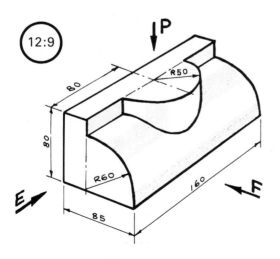

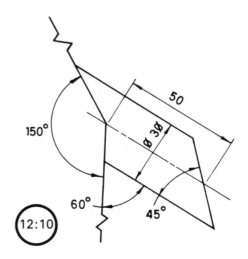

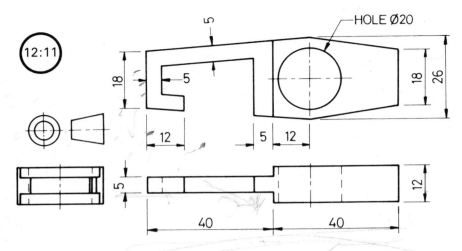

Q11 An orthographic projection of a reading lamp cable clip made from a plastics material is given in Fig. 12:11.

Make an accurate scale 2:1 **isometric** drawing of the clip. (*LU*)

Q12 Figure 12:12 is a drawing of a plastic stand. Make a full sized planometric drawing of the stand. Show edge A at 30° to the horizontal line. All dimensions are in millimetres. (*AEB*)

Q13 From point A on a straight promenade running North, a lighthouse is seen to be 45° East of North.

From point B, 800 metres further North on the promenade, the lighthouse is seen at 70° East of North.

(a) Find and state the shortest distance to the lighthouse from the promenade.

(b) At a point 4/7 of the distance from the lighthouse to point A lies a wreck. Find and show this point by construction and state its distance from the lighthouse.

(c) By construction, find and state the triangular area of sea between the lighthouse and points A and B. (*O & CSEB*)

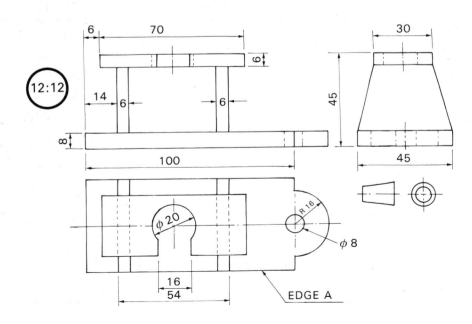

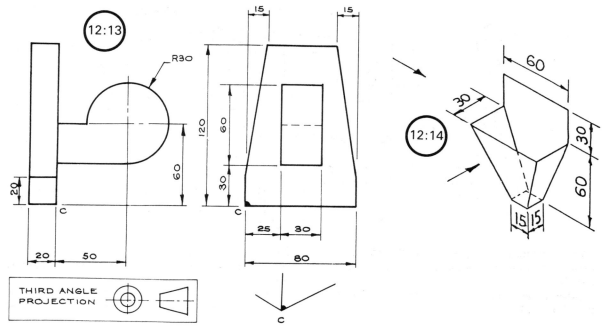

THIRD ANGLE PROJECTION

Q14 The orthographic drawings in Fig. 12:13 show two views of a **coat hook**.

Complete, **full size**, an **isometric drawing** of the coat hook using the given position for corner 'C'.

Do not include hidden detail. (*EMREB*)

Q15 The hopper for a waste disposal point is shown in Fig. 12:14. It consists of a flat metal backplate to which is fixed a single piece of sheet metal bent so that it forms the front and sides. To a scale of full size:

(a) Draw elevations as indicated by the arrows.

(b) Draw the one piece development of the metal required to make the front and sides. (*WJEC*)

Q16 A front and an end view of a door handle are given in Fig. 12:15. Make a scale 1:1 (full size) isometric drawing of the handle. The screws should not be included in your drawing. Hidden detail is not required. (*WMEB*)

Q17 A logogram (sign) for a firm of sports clothes manufacturers is shown in Fig. 12:16.

Copy the drawing full size. All constructions required to obtain a smooth outline must be shown. (*WMEB*)

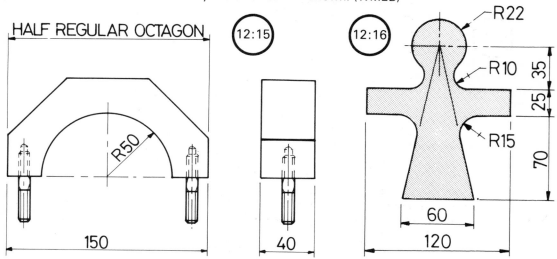

Q18 Figure 12:17 shows some of the water pipes used in a domestic water system. Solid lines represent the pipes. Cold water is supplied from the mains via a stop cock to a storage tank A, from there to a cylinder B and thence to the bottom of a boiler C. The water is then heated and rises via the pipe at the top of the boiler C to the cylinder B. Hot water can then be drawn off for the taps at the wash basin D, sink unit E, and the bath F. Cold water is supplied to the sink E by a branch pipe from the main supply pipe. The toilet, G, wash basin, D, and bath, F, are supplied from the tank A.

In the event of the water overheating it will continue to rise and be discharged into tank A.

Construct a circuit diagram of the system. Select and letter the most appropriate symbols from those given below and indicate by arrows the direction of the flow, and by colour which pipes are part of the hot water system and which are part of the cold water system.

Show the pipes leading to the taps but do not show the taps. (*AEB*)

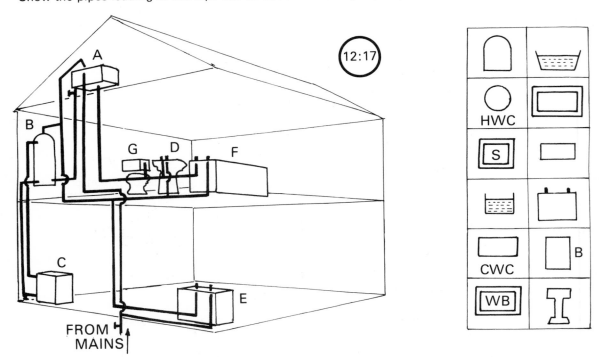

Q19 The following sequence of events occurs when a married couple get up in the morning. They have only one wash basin available.

Husband and wife get up together. The wife puts the kettle on, makes the tea, washes before her husband, gets dressed, cooks the breakfast, eats breakfast and washes up. The husband washes, shaves, gets dressed, eats breakfast, prepares to leave and leaves for the office.

The tea is made and whilst it brews the wife washes, gets dressed and cooks. Both sit down to breakfast at the same time.

Each activity takes one unit of time except cooking, eating breakfast and washing up which each take two units of time.

(a) Draw a **flow diagram**, using letters from the list below to represent activities, of the sequence of events detailed above.

(A) put kettle on; (B) make tea; (C) cook breakfast; (D) wash up; (E) husband gets up; (F) husband eats breakfast; (G) wife gets up; (H) wife gets dressed; (I) wife washes; (J) wife eats breakfast; (K) husband shaves; (L) husband leaves for office; (M) husband prepares to leave; (N) tea brews; (O) husband washes; (P) husband gets dressed.

(b) State the minimum number of units of time needed by the couple to complete the sequence. (*AEB*)

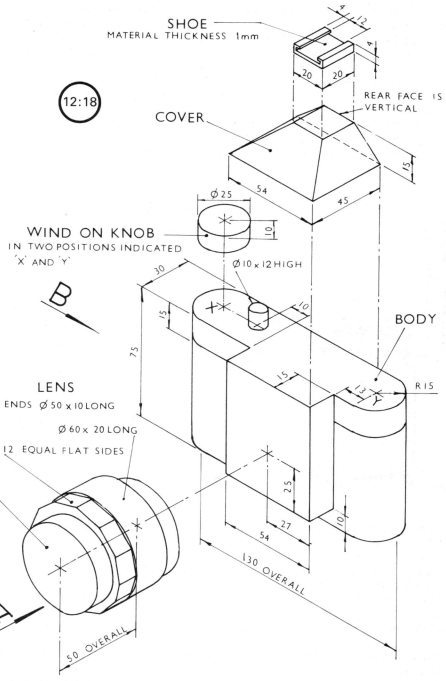

12:18
SHOE
MATERIAL THICKNESS 1mm
4
12
4
20
20
REAR FACE IS VERTICAL
COVER
15
54
45
Ø 25
10
WIND ON KNOB
IN TWO POSITIONS INDICATED 'X' AND 'Y'
Ø10 x 12 HIGH
30
B
15
10
75
BODY
15
13
R15
X
Y
LENS
ENDS Ø 50 x 10 LONG
Ø 60 x 20 LONG
12 EQUAL FLAT SIDES
25
27
54
10
130 OVERALL
A
50 OVERALL

Q20 The exploded pictorial view in Fig. 12:18 shows, in simplified outline, the parts of a **camera.**
Draw full size, in either first or third angle projection and with the parts fully assembled:

(a) A **front elevation** viewed in the direction of **arrow A.**
(b) A **plan** view.
(c) An **end elevation** viewed in the direction of **arrow B.**
(d) In a **title block**, print the title 'CAMERA', the scale of the drawing and the symbol of projection. (*SREB*)

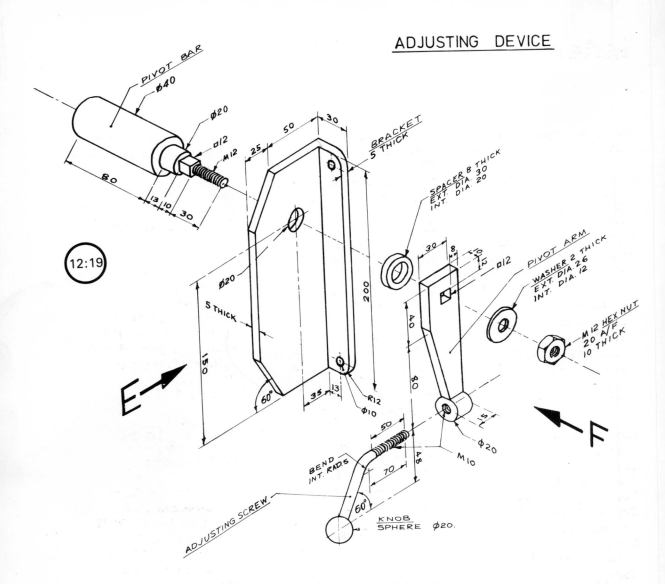

12:19

PIVOT BAR
Ø40
Ø20
Ø12
M12
80
13 10 30
25 50 30
BRACKET 5 THICK
SPACER 8 THICK
EXT. DIA. 30
INT. DIA. 20
Ø20
5 THICK
200
150
60°
35 13
R12
Ø10
30 8
Ø12
PIVOT ARM
WASHER 2 THICK
EXT. DIA. 26
INT. DIA. 12
M12 HEX NUT
20 A/F
10 THICK
40
80
Ø20
M10
BEND
INT. RADS
50
70
48
60°
ADJUSTING SCREW
KNOB
SPHERE Ø20.
E
F

Q21 The exploded drawing in Fig. 12:19 shows the details of an adjusting device.

(a) Draw, full size, in first angle or third angle orthographic projection the following views of the fully assembled device.
   (i) An elevation viewed from arrow F (no hidden detail required).
   (ii) An elevation viewed from arrow E complete with hidden detail.

(b) Draw in the lower right hand corner of your drawing a data box containing the following information:
   (i) The title
   (ii) The scale.
   (iii) The projection used.
   (iv) Your name.   (*NREB*)

Index